PRAISE FOR JOE ... *GIC*

"*Lodge Magic* humanizes t...   s against
the doors slammed shut by th...   ....w they re-open the doors is a
must read."

– THERESA CARUFEL, DIRECTOR, MINNESOTA BIO BRAIN ASSOCIATION

"I recognize myself in one of the characters this book. It makes me sad for whom
I used to be, and proud as hell of whom I have become."

– ANONYMOUS, LODGE MEMBER

"*Lodge Magic* informs, educates, and provides illumination into the inner fabric of
mental illness. The Tasks Model is an excellent concept which has returned dignity
and self-worth to my son's life. Finally, a program that works!"

– FRANK A.,PARENT OF A LODGE MEMBER

"*Lodge Magic* will help readers understand the power that people with mental
illness hold within themselves to change their lives. It dynamically presents how
people can actually thrive in the community, not just survive."

– JOSEPH MARRONE, INSTITUTE FOR COMMUNITY INCLUSION, BOSTON, MASSACHUSETTS

"Here is a band of people who beat the odds. *Lodge Magic* offers a rare glimpse
into the lives of those who have surmounted the insurmountable and created an
environment of friendship and shared responsibility."

– SHARON LUND, PRESIDENT, FALLS AGENCY — SISTER OF A PERSON WITH MENTAL ILLNESS

"It has always been the position of this researcher that simply moving patients
from the hospital to the community and maintaining them there is not sufficient
to establish a program's success. The degree to which real citizenship has been
achieved by the members of the Minneapolis lodge society is revealed in these
heartwarming stories."

– GEORGE W. FAIRWEATHER, PHD,RETIRED

"People with severe disabilities have hopes and dreams like everyone else. The
lodge is uniquely successful in helping people fulfill their dreams of being
productive, contributing members of society."

– PENNY STEELE, HENNEPIN COUNTY COMMISSIONER

"Lodge Magic can provide unexpected hope to anyone whose life, family, or
friends have been touched by mental illness. The rich human dimensions portrayed
by Trepp's stories suggest the immense potential of people suffering from mental
illness to lead fruitful and fulfilling lives. I wish that I had read such a book 20
years ago. "

– BOB CORRICK, RETIRED FINANCIAL MANAGER, BROTHER OF A PERSON WITH MENTAL ILLNESS

ACKNOWLEDGEMENTS

As this is my first book, I would be foolish not to mention Maureen, who for thirty years has been demanding evidence to support my literary pretensions exposed on our first date. In addition to Maureen's support, I am in debt to my friends Steve Kotz and Esther Onaga, who greeted my idea with enthusiasm and guided me in turning it into a book; and also to my editors, Lynn Thibodeau and Pat Pelto, and Sharon Lund at the Falls Agency. I am especially grateful to Beth Parkhill, who recognized me as a project in need of management, and volunteered her services as the project manager.

It would be appropriate to dedicate this book to Dr. Fairweather, the pioneering genius for whom the Fairweather Lodge model is named. It would be equally appropriate to dedicate it to Dorothy Berger, who founded Tasks Unlimited and continues as an active supporter, even in her retirement. The Tasks lodges, and therefore this book, would not exist without Fairweather and Berger. Nor would the Tasks lodge program have been as successful without the support of the federal HOME program, the Rehabilitation Services Branch of the Minnesota Department of Economic Security, or the Mental Health Divisions of Hennepin, Ramsey and Anoka Counties. I must acknowledge the assistance of (and it would not be inappropriate to dedicate the book to) the thirty-some lodge participants who enthusiastically provided material for this book.

But in final analysis, I must dedicate this book, the triumphant account of the Tasks Unlimited lodges, to all the men and women, over two hundred of them, who refused to allow mental illness to define their lives, and who chose instead to live, work, and prosper, making the lodge a success in the process.

LODGE MAGIC

*Real Life Adventures
in Mental Health Recovery*

BY JOHN K. TREPP

Published by Tasks Unlimited

For permission requests, write to the publisher at:
Tasks Unlimited
2419 Nicollet Avenue South
Minneapolis, MN 55407
Fax: 612-871-0432
www.tasksunlimited.org

Quantity sales and special discounts are available
on quantity purchases by corporations, associations, and others.

Trepp, John K., 1947
Lodge Magic

1. Fiction   2. Body, Mind & Spirit   3. Health & Fitness
4. Psychology & Psychiatry   5. Self-Help   6. Social Science
7. Mental Illness/schizophrenia 8. Social Entrepreneuring

I. Title II. Title: Real Life Adventures in Mental Health Recovery

Library of Congress Number 00-103761
ISBN 0-615-11435-0
PS3570.R438L6 2000   813.6

First Edition

 Printed on recycled paper.

Printed in the United States of America
05 2000   10 9 8 7 6 5 4 3 2 1

TABLE OF CONTENTS

PUBLISHER'S NOTE
Approximately thirty current or former Tasks Unlimited lodge members shared their life stories with the author specifically for use in this book. It is the collective hope of these individuals that *Lodge Magic* will, by inspiring lodge creation around the world, allow other people with mental illness to enjoy the productive, rewarding lives that they now enjoy.

Understandably, a few of these individuals were concerned about having their lives, especially the tragic parts before they found the lodge, made public. Out of respect for their privacy, all the names and many of the identifying details have been changed. Furthermore, most of the stories are composites; that is, the real experiences of two or more subjects are retold as though they happened to a single individual. As a result, any resemblance between actual persons and the fictionalized characters in these stories is purely coincidental.

FORWARD

By Dr. Esther Onaga

Given the current emphasis on consumer empowerment and recovery, this is a timely book of stories about men and women who have been labeled with some diagnosis of mental illness, and their unique paths to hopeful futures. The readers will meet memorable characters whose complex lives will reveal the multi-dimensionality and the immense human potential of people labeled "mentally ill."

About 1968, my attention was captured by the innovative research, funded by the National Institute of Mental Health (NIMH), on the Lodge, an intentional community providing housing, employment, and social support for people with psychiatric disabilities. The results were compelling. People who had a history of

THESE STORIES DEMONSTRATE HOW PARTICIPATION IN A LODGE SUPPORTS PEOPLE ON THEIR ROAD TO RECOVERY AND EMPOWERMENT.

long hospitalizations prior to their entry into the Lodge appeared to be able to live in the community and hold a job for longer periods of time in comparison to people who left the hospital for other types of community situations. Responding to the significant outcomes discovered in the model development study, NIMH funded two national studies to disseminate the results. The results of the dissemination research, from the viewpoint of the number of replicates, were dismal. The rational approach of disseminating research outcomes and providing technical support to those embracing change resulted in only a handful of adopters in the first study and another small group of adopters in the second study.

The project demonstrated how dissemination of positive results of an innovation, by itself, does not lead people to change practices, at least not in the mental health field. Clearly, the Lodge did not enjoy the same type of massive adoption experienced by innovations such as the polio vaccine or the use of personal computers.

The model, however, did take hold in a handful of places. Some of the original programs have disappeared for one reason or another, but programs in Arkansas, Idaho, Minnesota, and Ohio have survived to celebrate thirtieth anniversaries. And replications of these four programs have sprung up in other states.

The creator of the model, George W. Fairweather, known to his friends as Bill, was a maverick among his fellow psychologists. By conducting a series of experimental studies that showed these accomplishments were possible, he disproved the commonly held belief that people with long-term psychiatric hospitalization could not problem-solve in groups. He was unique in understanding the significance of societal values placed on employment, ownership of property, and money.

One story from Fairweather's early work demonstrates his courage to stand up for his commitment to the Lodge members regarding their full citizenship status. Some very distinguished people from Washington D.C. wanted to do a site visit. They called the Lodge and spoke to the only person who was at home at the

FAIRWEATHER UNDERSTOOD THAT PEOPLE WHO WERE MARGINALIZED BY THE LABEL OF "MENTAL ILLNESS" COULD DEFEAT THAT STIGMA ONLY BY EMULATING A MIDDLE-CLASS LIFESTYLE IN SITUATIONS IN WHICH THEY COULD EXERCISE SELF-DETERMINATION.

time. This Lodge member was reluctant to allow the group to come for a visit because he felt the members should decide as a group whether they wanted these visitors to come. The visitors, however, were insistent and said they would come for a short visit anyway and not to worry. Distraught with this information, the Lodge member decided to call the Lodge's attorney for advice. The attorney asked if the member wanted the visitors to come, and when the reply was, "I don't think so," the attorney instructed him to call the sheriff's office. The sheriff's car pulled up to the Lodge as the visitors drove in and they were asked to leave. Fairweather, when he heard the story, firmly supported the members for the decision. There were some chilly feelings for awhile about this renegade approach.

ONLY OVER TIME WERE THE VISITORS AND ADMINISTRATORS ABLE TO UNDERSTAND THE NEED TO KEEP THE INTEGRITY OF THE PROMISE THAT LODGE MEMBERS WERE FULL CITIZENS AND HAD THE RIGHTS OF ANY OTHER CITIZEN IN THE COMMUNITY.

Fairweather's personal life was similarly legendary. One such example is when he was summoned for jury duty. When interviewed, he asked if a guilty verdict would send the defendant to prison. The judge answered yes. Fairweather responded by saying that he could not, therefore, under any circumstances return a guilty verdict because he did not believe the current prison system was rehabilitative. The judge tried to lecture him about his citizenship duties; instead, Fairweather lectured him about the failures of the prison system. In the end, a frustrated judge dismissed him from the case.

This inclination to resist authority can be observed in Trepp as well. Of all the Lodges which have existed over the last thirty years, none has embodied the "Fairweather Spirit" more than Trepp's Tasks Unlimited Lodges. Repeatedly, Trepp has had to champion the Lodge principles among people who disapproved of employment as a rehabilitative strategy, and especially among people who argued against group living. Service delivery fads come and go in mental health, as they do in many fields. Through it all, however, it is clear that Trepp and his colleagues at Tasks have managed to maintain the core principles of the Lodge, to preserve the members' dignity, and to provide a sense of hope for the future.

> TREPP IS MUCH LIKE FAIRWEATHER IN HIS WILLINGNESS TO CHALLENGE THE CONVENTIONAL WISDOM, ESPECIALLY WHEN THE CONVENTIONAL WISDOM WORKS AGAINST THE INTERESTS OF DISADVANTAGED PEOPLE.

Through his captivating stories about the lives of Lodge members, Trepp provides another perspective with which to view the work of George W. Fairweather. The statistics of the original experiment speak convincingly about the effectiveness of the Lodge model. But Trepp, through his exquisite crafting of stories, conveys a more complete picture of the diverse individuals served in the Lodge and the richness of their robust lives.

The stories reveal the Lodge members' pride in being able to drive a car, own a house, take vacations, and eat out with friends, to buy presents for loved ones — activities of "normal" adulthood. Most important, and encouraging among people with psychiatric disabilities, they have a sense of hopefulness about the future. They live in a beautiful home, but they are planning improvements or additions. They have good jobs, but they expect raises and promotions. They are saving money and making plans for retirement.

At a minimum, readers will gain a sense of the humanity of the individuals who live with psychiatric disabilities. Readers will be less inclined to see people as stereotypes when they encounter someone with a label such as schizophrenia, bi-polar disorder, or depression. And some readers, empowered by the phenomenal success of Tasks Unlimited's Lodge program, will challenge the discouraging assumptions of their local mental health system, as Fairweather and Trepp have done. Trepp has not provided us with detailed instructions of how to change things, but he inspires us to demand a better system than we have come to accept.

Dr. Onaga is a Professor of Family and Child Ecology at Michigan State University and Director of the Michigan Transition Evaluation Initiative. She also serves on the national Board of Directors of the Coalition for Community Living and the International Association for Psychosocial Rehabilitation Services.

PREFACE

In 1978, I had the good fortune to be fired from an undistinguished position in an undistinguished community mental health program. Because jobs were hard to find in 1978, and my wife, Maureen, was pregnant with our second child, I did not immediately recognize the fortune of this event. Desperate to support my family, and totally ignorant of what I was getting into, I took a job as the Director of the Tasks Unlimited Lodge Program. As I assume is true of most of my readers, I had never heard of Tasks Unlimited or the Fairweather Lodge Model.

Quite by accident, I had stumbled on to an amazing collection of people — people whose diagnoses suggested extreme mental illnesses, people with horrible side-effects from the psychotropic medications available at that time, people with colorful histories — people who, in spite of all these barriers, were model citizens, going to work, maintaining their homes, paying their bills. Most amazing of all, they were living, working and supporting each other in little communal groups, with the most minimal assistance from professionals. No one had told them that it couldn't work, and so they made it work.

By 2000, Tasks was sponsoring sixteen lodges, providing homes to eighty people. These people, some of whom have agreed to share their stories for this book, continue to lead rich, productive lives, completely at odds with the dismal statistics regarding people with serious mental illness.

Most of the people in this book, and most people living in Tasks lodges, are diagnosed with schizophrenia. While less common than depression, schizophrenia is a relatively common condition (more common than AIDS, for example) afflicting approximately one percent of the population, roughly three million Americans. And, as some of the stories in this book will illustrate, it is a devastating condition, capable of destroying not only the life of the person who has it, but often the lives of those close to the person as well.

Part of the problem in understanding schizophrenia is that it is less a disease than a diagnostic category. Worse yet, schizophrenia is a diagnosis one gets as a result of negative-indicator testing, *i.e.*, other things getting ruled out. At the risk of oversimplification, the test goes like this: if you are acting strange and you are not intoxicated, high, stupid, or in trauma, and the odd behavior persists over time, you will be suspected of schizophrenia. The final criterion is that you have to be broke (rich people can afford a more hopeful diagnosis). A layman's definition of the Latin word "schizophrenia" could be, "Out of money, acts goofy, and we don't know why."

We have no cure for schizophrenia. Some research suggests that by a certain age, perhaps fifty, schizophrenia fades away. I know that this is not true for everyone with this diagnosis, because I know people in their sixties and seventies who retain some of their florid symptoms. But it may well be true, and it is definitely encouraging, to hear that some people will outlive their schizophrenia.

However, even if it is true that people don't get schizophrenia until age twenty and it goes away by age fifty, that's still thirty years. Imagine having a horrible disease for thirty years. Now imagine having a debilitating disease for the thirty years of your life that are supposed to be your most productive years. Your contemporaries have acquired a lifetime supply of adult friendships built on common interests; you have no friends, only doctors and social workers. They have husbands or wives (at least ex-husbands or ex-wives); you have neither. They have financial assets; some of them are actually rich; you have spent your adult life on welfare, explicitly prohibited from acquiring assets. Your contemporaries have skills, they know how to talk to people, how to dance, how to repair a boat, how to cook; you were afraid to talk to people, you never owned a boat, and the kitchen where you lived was off-limits to "residents." Worst of all, your fellow seniors have identities based on who they were. They are Cathy's father, Bobby's grandmother, the former general manager of the company, the long-time president of the PTA, or one of the guys who built such and such a building. You are the ex-mental patient. Welcome to your golden years!

Schizophrenia is one of several diagnoses generally lumped into the category of "serious mental illness." Some of the characters in this book have other forms of serious mental illness such as depression, bi-polar disorder or manic-depression (an obsolete term for bi-polar disorder), or schizo-affective disorder, which in layman's language is a cross between schizophrenia and bipolar disorder. Depression is an extremely common disease, some estimates ranging as high as twenty percent of the population, and can be extremely debilitating. Fortunately, the pharmacological treatment of depression is advanced, in comparison to that of schizophrenia, so that hundreds of thousands of Americans can, with the minor inconvenience of medications, lead normal lives in spite of their depression. Some depression is not as easily treated with medications alone. Some people with depression or related diseases require extraordinary support, as is generally true of people with schizophrenia.

I have tried in this book to tell the real stories of a unique group of people who have managed, for over thirty years, to provide each other with the extraordinary support they each need. These are the life stories, the success stories, of the Tasks Unlimited lodge members. They are stories of people with debilitating diseases who have refused to be debilitated. They make friends by being a friend. They acquire skills by learning from their mistakes. They get ahead financially by going to work everyday, even when they would rather sleep in. And they do it together. They argue, they criticize, they nag. They also encourage, they care, they sacrifice, and in the end, they celebrate together.

Some lodge members began life in a foster home or a reform school. Others began with more promise — star athlete, prep school socialite, medical student. All of them crashed to society's bottom rung when stricken with major illnesses such as schizophrenia. But these are not stories of despair and tragedy; these are victory celebrations.

"She wasn't famous,
but she should have been."

JoEllen Richardson
Lilac Lodge

CHAPTER ONE

A QUEEN'S FUNERAL

As she listened to Rev. Anderson's eulogy, JoEllen thought about the first time she saw Susie in the chapel at St. Helen's. JoEllen had arrived just in time for chapel and was seated in a row of freshmen who she could tell were just as scared as she was.

Across the aisle and up a couple of rows she noticed a group of girls who seemed so mature, so confident, so sophisticated, that JoEllen assumed they were all seniors. Susie, the blondest, most mature, confident, sophisticated-looking girl of them all, was the center of their attention. JoEllen knew right away that Susie was the queen of the school. JoEllen was shocked to learn later that these popular, confident girls were a mixture of juniors and seniors, and that Susie was only a sophomore.

But she was the queen, the real queen. Some of the girls, only a few, were prettier. Some of the girls, only a few, were better students. Almost all of the girls had wealthier parents and

1

better clothes to wear when uniforms weren't required. But Susie was clearly the most popular girl at St. Helen's Academy, and JoEllen learned that Susie possessed the single most crucial qualification for royalty.

Susie was gracious. Most of the sophomores wouldn't talk to freshmen except to tease or make fun of them, but Susie would. When the slow girls got an answer wrong in algebra, most of the smart girls would roll their eyes and groan as though it were physically painful to sit in the same room with such dunces, but Susie would offer to show them how to do the problem after class.

Once, when they went to St. Kevin's for a dance, Sister Irene, who got in trouble for it later, said they could wear lipstick. They all put it on, some for the first time. Rachael, who was horse-faced to begin with, made an awful mess of it. The pretty girls who knew how to wear lipstick whispered about it on the bus, loud enough for everyone to hear. When they got to the dance, Susie sat next to Rachael. Every boy at St. Kevin's wanted to dance with Susie. When they would ask her she would explain that Rachael was her best friend and they had agreed not to dance unless both were asked. The clever boys would find a friend and come back.

Susie's biological father was a wealthy banker. Susie's mother was very moody and her parents used to have terrible fights. They were divorced when Susie was seven. Susie's father threatened to go to court and say that her mother wasn't fit to raise the children. Susie's mother was so scared she signed a settlement agreeing to no alimony or even any child support. She supported her three kids by waitressing. Later, however, Susie's paternal grandmother paid Susie's tuition at St. Helen's.

When Susie's father died, he left half of his estate to his second wife, and half (about $900,000) in a trust fund for Susie, her brother and sister. Because he didn't want Susie's mother to benefit from it, he set up the trust so that the children couldn't get the money until their mother died. Later on, Susie was advised to challenge the provisions of the trust, but declined to do so out of respect for her father's wishes. When Susie couldn't afford to go to college, one of the other girls who knew about the trust fund remarked that Susie would be better off if her mother were dead. Susie got angry and said it was the most horrible thing she had ever heard anyone say. She loved her mother and prayed for her health every night. She said she didn't really care about college anyway.

JoEllen did not see Susie for almost ten years after St. Helen's, but she never forgot her. Although her appearance had changed a lot, JoEllen recognized her as soon as she stepped out of the van in front of the Lilac Lodge. She was thinner and paler than she had been in prep school. Susie's beautiful blond hair had turned to dishwater and it was cut in an awkward style, making her look much older than twenty-seven. Worst of all, the confidence was gone. The bubbly girl whose radiance used to dominate a room had somehow turned into a timid-looking woman.

JoEllen gasped when she realized that Susie was the new girl moving in. JoEllen felt overwhelming sadness to think that Susie's trademark graciousness had been swallowed up by mental illness, right along with her blond hair and confidence. JoEllen's own losses, great as they were, seemed less tragic than the thought that Susie's heroic graciousness had been compromised, even a little. God, how she hated mental illness at that moment.

Shortly after her nineteenth birthday, Susie experienced the first of what would become recurring bouts of severe depression. Sometimes Susie's depression was so severe she couldn't care for herself and would end up in the hospital. Eventually

Susie was sent to Rochester State Hospital for shock treatment. Initially the shock treatment seemed to cure the depression and Susie was able to return to her waitress job and her studies at the business college. But each time the depression would return and the cycle would start over. The doctors told Susie the memory loss she experienced was a temporary side effect of the shock treatment. After her third series of treatments at age twenty-four, Susie realized that both her memory and her concentration were progressively worse after each cycle. Whether from the depression or the treatment she wasn't sure. As a result, Susie didn't recognize her schoolmate until JoEllen told her who she was.

As it turned out, however, Susie's graciousness was undamaged.

Just as the girls at St. Helen's had been, the entire Lilac Lodge was soon captivated by Susie's graciousness. The lodge members all earned their living as janitors. When Gloria complained about how hard the work was, Susie would point out that, whereas some people bought expensive machines or health club memberships for the chance to work up a sweat, the Lilacs got paid for sweating. Then Susie would offer to help Gloria with her route.

Tilly, though she was from a more modest background than St. Helen's, used to complain that cleaning restrooms was beneath her; she should be working in one of these offices and someone else should be cleaning her restroom, because she was a high school graduate. Susie would always say it wasn't so bad and point out the relaxed pace, the low pressure, the satisfaction of making things shine and sparkle. In encouragement, never reprimand, Susie would point out how lucky they were to have steady work and a nice home when so many people had neither. And when household responsibilities were divided up at Lilac Lodge, Susie would volunteer for the bathroom.

JoEllen had been a member of the Lilac Lodge for two-and-a-half years when Susie moved in. Most of the girls had been members longer, Gloria and Tilly almost ten years. Up to that point, there had not been much formal entertaining. Gloria and Tilly dated some, but the men were Gloria and Tilly's guests, not lodge company.

Several Lilacs had relatives who would come by, but generally just to pick up or drop off their family member on the way to a family birthday, holiday, or maybe out to eat. Occasionally someone's relative would visit at the lodge, but usually quietly, semi-privately, in the den. JoEllen had seen Tilly's brother, for example, a dozen times over two-and-a-half years, but had never spoken beyond "hello" and "Tilly will be down in a minute."

Susie began to change these patterns immediately. Despite her occasionally severe depression, Susie had maintained a close relationship with a girl named Joan from her business college days. Joan was married and had a three-year-old daughter when Susie joined the Lilacs. Joan came to visit Susie often. She never brought her husband but she frequently brought her delightful daughter, Jackie.

Susie would entertain Joan and little Jackie in the kitchen, the rec room, wherever the other Lilacs were. Some of the others, had they been so fortunate as to have a friend like Joan, would have wanted all her attention, but not Susie. Joan and Jackie soon became friends with all the Lilacs. If Joan and Susie wanted to go to Toby's Restaurant for coffee and pie, they would always invite others along.

Under Susie's leadership, minor holidays soon became party occasions. New Year's Eve, SuperBowl Sunday, St. Patrick's Day, May Day, the Fourth of July, and especially Halloween. Susie had been a promising artist at St. Helen's and had a special flair for crafts and decorating. She would draw the other Lilacs into her projects and give each one an assignment. Susie made each one feel as though her assignment was the most critical piece of the project. Newspaper, egg cartons, bottle caps, grapevine, wildflowers, yarn, and crepe paper would be transformed into spectacular decorations appropriate to the season.

The first Halloween, Susie invited the Hiawatha Lodge, a co-ed group who helped the Lilacs clean the County Courthouse, and the party was a tremendous success. By the following Halloween, all the other lodges were invited, and most came. By the third Halloween, the party included neighbors, Tasks staff, and people who worked at the courthouse.

The other Lilacs would have been content to invite people in person, and to call the ones they never saw, and that might have been sufficient. But Susie insisted on formal invitations which she would personally design, copy at Kinkos, and mail out. Cindy, the Lilac Lodge Coordinator, pointed out that they could run the copies at the Tasks office and distribute almost all through the Tasks or courthouse mail, or by walking around the block. But Susie didn't feel this was proper, even though it would have saved money. Susie would offer to pay the cost of copying and postage out of her personal funds, but the Lilacs would always vote to pay it out of the lodge treasury.

Although all the parties were a hit, the annual Halloween Party was the event of the year. Halloween was Susie's favorite holiday, even ahead of Christmas. Susie would spend all year collecting ideas from magazines, scraps for decorations, and odd pieces of clothing for costumes.

All the Lilacs would be in costume, most of Susie's design, and there would be a prize (usually a homemade pie to take home) for the best-costumed guest. Sometimes Susie would have to explain to Tilly why she could not, for reasons of etiquette, win their own prize even though the hosts typically out-costumed the guests. JoEllen would observe, as if it were necessary, that none of the guests had Susie helping them dress.

The food served at the Lilac parties was as elaborate as the decorations — excessive, according to Cindy. There were always one or two men, Chuckie from the Spirits, for example, who had been institutionalized a long time, and would really pig out. The Lilacs would prepare snacks for thirty people and Chuckie or somebody would eat half of it and the food would run out. Next party, the Lilacs would prepare snacks for fifty people and Chuckie would still eat half of it and the food would run out again.

Food for the ever-growing parties became a major item in the Lilac budget. The lodge shoppers would scrimp and save for weeks to put a little cushion in the lodge treasury, then a party would come along and Susie would talk the lodge into blowing every dime. Sometimes the treasury wouldn't fully recover from one party before another would come along.

Part of Cindy's responsibility was to advise lodge members on issues related to financial management, both personal and group. Cindy would argue that since certain members of certain lodges were pigs, and there wasn't any acceptable way to disin-vite specific people, the logical solutions were to go cheap on snacks (popcorn and Kool-aid for example), or ask others to bring food.

Susie was horrified by both suggestions. "You don't invite people to a party and then tell them to bring food." Popcorn was okay for the SuperBowl if served with peanuts, chips, raw vegetables and dip, but you had to serve hot dogs on the Fourth and oysters on New Year's Eve. Kool-aid was out of the ques-tion; lemonade was okay on the Fourth, but you had to serve champagne on New Year's Eve and green beer on St. Patrick's Day, plus coffee for the drivers and members who didn't (or weren't allowed to) drink.

Cindy's role as "staff" conferred considerable influence over the group, and sometimes she could bend the group toward moderation. But no one could bear to see Susie disappointed, and Susie was the queen of the lodge.

Susie's diagnosis was manic depression and she did experience occasional episodes of mania, but mostly she suffered from chronic low-level depression. In addition to prescription medications, coffee seemed to help, the stronger the better. All the Lilacs loved their coffee, but especially Susie. The lodge would go through two big pots every morning, and early afternoon would find half of the Lilacs at Toby's drinking coffee. The third pot of the day would be brewed as soon as the Lilacs returned from work. Often as not, Susie or Gloria would brew a fourth pot after supper, and the two of them, maybe others, would sit up half the night drinking it. Cindy, Dr. Bob, and Darcy, the lodge social worker, tried to convince Susie it was the coffee that kept her up all night, and that coffee wasn't good for her.

Dr. Bob knew Susie was using coffee to help medicate her depression, and frequently suggested increasing her Lithium as a replacement for the coffee, but Susie resisted. She didn't really have any unpleasant side effects from the dose of Lithium she took, she just liked coffee better. Lithium was just a pill, but coffee was a social drug, and Susie loved to socialize. Sometimes Susie and Gloria would sit in the kitchen of the otherwise dark lodge, rarely talking because the rest were sleeping, just smoking and drinking coffee. The coffee and Gloria's silent company helped Susie survive many a depressed night.

Eventually, it was the coffee acid, rather than the caffeine, that killed Susie. It ate away the lining of her stomach and started the cancer. Maybe she would have gotten stomach cancer anyway (and as a smoker she was obviously at risk for lung cancer) but several of the Lilacs felt guilty for having shared so many pots of coffee with her. They all knew Dr. Bob had wanted her to cut back. After the funeral, Rev. Anderson gave them absolution.

Susie learned she had cancer about eight months before she died. The first month she kept it a secret between herself and Cindy. Then she told the Lilacs. Most had guessed that something was seriously wrong. Susie, who had always been thin, was losing weight, and they all knew that she had gone in for tests. Susie was different afterwards, not more depressed really, maybe less, but different in a way they couldn't describe.

For a while she continued to work every day. She didn't have to, of course, but she preferred it to being alone in the lodge while the rest were at work. Everett, the Crew Chief from Hiawatha Lodge, switched Susie to an easier route, and everyone tried to help her.

Tilly would go to the supply closet a couple of minutes before their 3 p.m. start time and set up Susie's cart for her. Susie's new route was part of Gloria's old route, so Gloria would walk it ahead of her and take care of anything unusual or problematic. Hiawatha Lodge pitched in also; everyone made certain Susie's work would be as easy as possible.

In August, Susie was hospitalized for more tests. JoEllen was with her when the doctor shared the news that the cancer was spreading fast. JoEllen took it very hard, screaming "No! No!" over and over. Susie was quiet and comforted JoEllen.

Susie didn't need to stay in the hospital, but she needed daily nursing services. The doctor gave her the choice of a residential hospice program or outpatient hospice services at the lodge. Susie chose to stay at the Lilacs.

The hospice workers offered to teach the Lilacs ways to ensure that Susie took her medicine, but the Lilacs were experts and taught the hospice workers a few tricks. The hospice did teach Cindy and the Lilacs how to help Susie bathe and eat. It was important for her to eat as much as possible for as long as possible to keep her strength up. They weighed her every day. The doctor said what she ate mattered less than to keep her eating, so they all made Susie's favorite foods, and Shirley from Flagstone Lodge sent over her famous brownies. Frequently she had no appetite at all, nor any particular interest in prolonging the inevitable, but she would force herself to eat a little because she knew how much trouble her friends were going to on her behalf.

The Lilacs decided Susie should never be alone, so they set up rotating shifts. They took turns staying home from work, and each night someone would sleep in an armchair next to Susie's bed. No one seemed to mind. If anything, Lilac Lodge became more peaceful and cooperative than ever before. Later, in discussion with Cindy and Dr. Bob, Gloria and Tilly described feeling stressed by Susie's final weeks, but Susie complained so little that the others tried to complain even less.

Susie's brother and sister both came to visit during her final weeks at the lodge. Each lived out of state, and although they always called on Christmas and her birthday, she had not seen either in person for a long time. Susie's sister spent two nights at the lodge; Gloria gave up her room and slept on a cot in Tilly's room. Susie's brother, who was a successful stock broker, stayed in a fancy hotel downtown, but for two days he stayed with Susie while they all went to work. Susie really enjoyed seeing him.

Susie's mother, who was recently married for the fifth time and living on the West coast, never came. Susie said her health wouldn't allow it (her sister said their mother was too busy with her new husband).

When Susie became completely unable to eat, she was hospitalized so they could feed her intravenously. The Lilacs had to visit in shifts because there was not enough space in the hospital room for the whole lodge to visit at once. None of the Lilacs was present when Susie died late on October 28. She was forty-four.

Cindy called Susie's mother to give her the news and ask about arrangements. Her mother asked to have Susie cremated and the ashes sent to her. She said she and Susie's brother and sister would hold a private memorial service the next time they got together, but she wasn't certain when that would be since they were so spread out. Cindy volunteered the Lilacs to host a public service in Minneapolis, but Susie's mother said emphatically that it would serve no purpose.

Naturally, the Lilacs held a service anyway. At first they voted not to notify Susie's three living relatives. At the last minute they changed their mind and invited Susie's brother and sister. Neither came, but Susie's sister sent the Lilacs a lengthy letter thanking them for having a service and for all they had done. The sister's letter implied an assumption on her part that the service had been small and intimate, probably just the Lilacs and that one friend of Susie's.

Intimate perhaps, but hardly small. Over one hundred people crowded into Lilac Lodge for the service. They didn't all fit in the living room. There were people in the kitchen, the hall, even on the back porch straining to hear.

All but one of the Hiawathans came, and at least one member from every lodge. Fifteen or twenty staff came, several neighbors and people from the courthouse. Former lodge members and staff came also. Joan brought her husband, her mother, and two other ladies no one else recognized. The Lilacs put up some of the decorations they had made for the cancelled

Halloween party. Several of the lodges brought home-made salads or desserts and Tasks bought Kentucky Fried Chicken.

Besides being a Lutheran minister, Rev. Anderson was a judge at the County Courthouse where the Lilacs worked, so he knew Susie and most of the Lilacs. He said a lot of nice things about Susie. He said he had no inside information as to who went to heaven and who didn't, but he had studied the Bible for many years, and it was his opinion that Susie was the type of person who had the best possible chance.

Rev. Anderson closed with a prayer and then invited anyone else who wanted to speak to do so. JoEllen spoke. She wanted to say that she wished Susie had outlived her mom, even if only by a couple of years, because then she could have inherited her share of her father's money and she could have lived in the style which she deserved. But JoEllen knew Susie wouldn't approve of that sentiment, so she just said she hoped to meet up with Susie again some day. She said she was going to try to be a better person than she sometimes had been so she could go to heaven where Susie probably was. And if Susie was someplace else, that's where she wanted to go too, because heaven couldn't be all that great if Susie wasn't there.

> *"The sheriff said to the deputy, 'Looks like we got another Phil Larson,' and I thought, 'Wow!'"*
>
> **Charles "Chuckie" Lundquist**
> **Spirit Lodge**

CHAPTER TWO

LEGENDS OF SPICER

Chuckie and Phil grew up together in Spicer, Minnesota, population 2,915. They weren't close because they were four years apart, which is a lot when you're growing up. But they knew each other because everybody in Spicer knows each other. As it turned out, they had a couple of things in common.

Phil was aware of Chuckie but he didn't pay much attention to him. Just another little kid hanging around, getting in the way from time to time. His main memory of him was that he thought Chuckie turned him and Leonard in when they were snowballing cars. He and Leonard would have been twelve at the time, and Chuckie about eight.

He and Leonard had a perfect spot for snowballing cars. They used to stand between the grain elevator at the edge of town and the outside wall of the hardware store. They were barely visible to the cars coming into town on 23, and then only if the drivers were looking for them, which of course they weren't. The boys could see the cars coming, though, and judge their speed and their deceleration as they entered town. By the time the cars reappeared in the narrow opening between the elevator and the store, the high-lobbed snowballs were already in the air, falling toward their intended targets. The boys would peek over the top of a row of oil drums to watch the results.

Half the drivers had snowballed cars from the same spot in their youth and didn't get too excited about the bombardment. The other half would stop in front of the hardware store, and back up to the opening in an attempt to identify the source of the attack. Once in awhile, the school principal, or some eighteen or nineteen year-old trying to impress his girlfriend, might park in front of the store and round the corner running hard toward the oil drums. This was the most fun of all because the boys would have anticipated the threat and retreated to one of a dozen hiding places in the sheds or trucks or woods behind. It was the perfect spot.

They weren't the only ones to use it, even then, but Phil and Leonard were the town's most dedicated snowballers at the time. Younger boys, including Chuckie, would hang around to watch, but they didn't have enough arm to reach the road from the protective oil drums, and the older boys would ridicule any failed attempts.

Chuckie was the only little kid around, however, the day Leonard scored a direct hit on Mrs. Ellenberg's windshield, startling her into nicking a parked car. So they both figured it was Chuckie who turned them in. Chuckie denied it the next day at recess, and forty years later he still denies it, but Phil still thinks he did.

Chuckie, on the other hand, was very much aware of and impressed by the older Phil. Phil was hip. Or as close to hip as

14

existed in Spicer in those days. Phil had a B.A., a D.A., a P.C., and a tattoo.

The B.A. was slang for a Bad Attitude; Phil was famous for his.

The D.A. was a haircut, so named because the back of your head looked like the south end of a duck swimming north. You couldn't get a D.A. in Spicer. There were only two barbers, and neither wanted to offend their respectable customers by contributing to teen delinquency. So any boy wanting a D.A. had to get his haircut in Green Lake.

P.C. was slang, then, for a pack of Camels. But it referred only to a pack of Camels carried in a turned-up sleeve of a white T-shirt. The T-shirt had to be white, because otherwise the Camels wouldn't show. Phil wore a P.C. all the time. School was the really hip part. You couldn't have smokes in school, but Phil would walk into school every day with a P.C. showing through the turned-up left sleeve of his T-shirt, right above the tattoo. (The tattoo was hip too. He got it in Minneapolis when he was only fifteen. It was a heart, and inside the heart were the letters "IRMA." Phil didn't actually know anyone named Irma, that's what made it so hip.) The teachers would see the P.C. and the tattoo, and yell "Phillip Larson! Give me those cigarettes right now!"

Phil would say, "What cigarettes, sir?" or "ma'am?"

"You know what cigarettes. The cigarettes right there in your sleeve!"

"I don't have any cigarettes," he would say, unrolling his sleeve to produce what appeared to be a full pack of Camels. The teacher would angrily snatch the pack from him, only to find that it was full of Kleenex or grass clippings or something. Phil had his real Camels stashed outside somewhere. Phil was a legend.

Part of the legend was the two cars he owned at age sixteen. He drove around town in a '52 Chevy which had been in a wreck before he bought it. The whole right side was caved in at least a foot. Neither right-side door was operable. To ride with Phil you had to climb in through the front right window, which was always open because the glass was missing. Or you could enter through the left rear door and climb over the massive bench seat. The whole frame was bent so that the right front wheel pointed out and the right rear wheel pointed in, neither of them parallel to the left wheels. He went through a lot of re-tread tires.

His other car didn't run most of the time, but it was one of the classic rides of all time, a '42 Lincoln Zephyr Convertible. It was canary yellow with a black ragtop and black and yellow cowhide upholstery. It had a V-12 engine and a Zephyr Stick. (Phil insists that a Zephyr Stick, whatever its function, was a wonderful thing to have. Phil also reports that his '42 Zephyr weighed 5800 pounds, without passengers, luggage or fuel.)

The central theme of the Phil Larson legend, however, and the reason that no one in Spicer will ever forget him, was that he killed his stepmother and stepaunt. And it wasn't just that he killed them, it was the way he killed them.

Phil never talks about it much, but Chuckie remembers it well. It was in the *Spicer Sentinel*. Actually, it was the only story in the *Sentinel* for weeks, and it was the only thing people talked about for months.

He killed them with a fireplace poker. He beat them over the head with it, repeatedly. The county coroner said Phil killed his stepmother first, then his stepaunt, and then came back and whacked his stepmother a few more times. In the initial story in the *Sentinel*, the coroner claimed that he had clubbed his stepmother about a dozen times, then his stepaunt fifteen or sixteen times, and then his stepmother about six times more. In the weeks to follow the coroner backed off from the specific number of blows, but stuck with the stepmother-stepaunt-stepmother theory.

One of the reasons Chuckie remembers it all so clearly is that he was over at Phil's house that very day. The next day too. Of course everybody in town was there the next day, gawking at the blood-splattered living room and the bloody footprints in the kitchen. Chuckie was there the day of the incident, before it happened.

It was a warm Saturday afternoon in May. Phil was working on the Zephyr. The Holmgren brothers were kind of helping. Mostly they were teasing him about his girlfriend going out with a guy from Green Lake. Phil got hot about the teasing. Chuckie always figured the teasing and the girlfriend were factors in what happened that evening.

Phil doesn't remember Chuckie being there that day. He says, "Chuckie might have come by with some other kids. Me and Doug Holmgren were trying to set the timing on the Zephyr. We didn't have the right tools. We might have talked about a girl named Helen that I'd dated a couple of times; at that time she was dating a guy from Green Lake. But I don't remember it even came up that day. It sure didn't have anything to do with me killing my stepmother and aunt. They deserved what they got."

It was no longer a daily topic, but people were still occasionally discussing the Larson/Cook murders four years later when Chuckie killed his stepmother and his three-year-old half-sister.

The two events are indelibly linked in Spicer history. They were the only double homicides ever, almost the only homicides period. Both took place in May. Both boys had just turned sixteen. Both killed their stepmothers and one other person. (Phil joked later that most of the guys in Shakopee had killed their stepmothers and anyone who tried to stop them: the mailman, a pizza delivery guy, whoever. "Stay out of rooms with women and their sixteen year-old stepsons," he advises.)

Chuckie was a lot less messy. He shot each one of them once with his father's deer rifle. He tried to turn it on himself, but it took a long time to get up the nerve to pull the trigger, even with his eyes closed, so all he got was a piece of his ear. He screamed in pain and threw down the rifle. He couldn't find the nerve to try again.

He felt real bad about his baby sister, whom he loved. He cried over her body until the sheriff came. To this day he cannot explain why he killed her. "I guess I didn't know what would happen to her, or who would take care of her, with Nancy and me both dead."

Chuckie and Phil did not see each other for several years.

Phil was immediately diagnosed with schizophrenia and sent to the state security hospital for the criminally insane at Shakopee. His brother and his sister used to visit him once in a while. Neither one of them lived in Spicer by the time of Chuckie's incident, but they both heard about it and the parallels people were drawing. Phil's brother and sister agreed with him that the incidents were significantly dissimilar. In all his rage, he would never have killed an innocent child.

The townspeople of Spicer, sensing a trend, demanded harsher treatment of Chuckie lest there be a third copy. He was certified as an adult and convicted twice of murder, once in the first degree and once in the second. He observed later that the prison was a nicer facility than Shakopee; better gym, better library. Both were a little scary at first, and real boring.

"Shakopee was worse before Chuckie got there," says Phil.
"Before they got Prolixin and Haldol, all they had was Thorazine
and Stelazine, which is really the same thing, and it didn't work
on everybody. If a guy in your cell, twenty guys to a cell, was
hallucinating and screaming after lockdown, the bulls would
turn the fire hose on him. Likely as not he would run around
the cell trying to avoid the water but the water would follow
him. By the time the bulls got tired of it, everybody and everything in there was wet. And you'd stay wet and cold until the
next morning; there was no way to dry off or get warm. One
guy caught pneumonia and died from it, and he wasn't even
the guy they were hosing down."

After five years in prison, Chuckie was diagnosed with
schizophrenia and transferred to Shakopee. (Later, his murder
convictions were set aside on the grounds that he had never
been given a proper psychiatric evaluation.) He was glad to see
Phil. He didn't exactly consider him a friend at that point, but
he was the only familiar face at Shakopee. They wound up
working in the kitchen together and became friends.

Shakopee was full of people who had killed someone,
mostly their mothers, and most were gentle as lambs afterward.
But there were exceptions; the worst was Big Swede. Big Swede
had killed several people with his bare hands, two more since he
got to Shakopee. When he wasn't in restraints, he was inclined
to pick people up and throw them around. The patient council
passed a motion requesting that Big Swede be kept permanently
in restraints, but the hospital wouldn't do it. Phil was the only
patient in the hospital that Big Swede liked; not even Phil knew
why. Anyway, Phil told Big Swede that Chuckie was okay and
he shouldn't hurt him, and Big Swede never did.

Chuckie got out of Shakopee after only eleven years. They
transferred him to the locked unit at Mendota, and after a year
he was transferred to the unlocked unit to begin discharge plan-

ning. No one was discharged from Shakopee in those days.

The criminal justice system wasn't through with Chuckie, however. His convictions had been set aside, but there is no statute of limitations on murder. The prosecutor in Kandiyohi County heard about his potential discharge, and threatened to retry Chuckie. But Chuckie's lawyer discovered that the County Prosecutor didn't really care if Chuckie got out, he just wanted to be certain he stayed far away from Kandiyohi County. Which was fine with Chuckie. He pleaded guilty to two counts of third-degree murder and was sentenced to the time already served and lifetime parole.

Instead of a community mental health facility, he was discharged to a half-way house operated by the corrections system. He stayed there ninety days as prescribed. His parole officer (P.O.) found him a job as a dishwasher at a Minneapolis hotel and an apartment nearby.

Things did not go too well. He had thrown his meds away the third day at the half-way house when he realized no one cared if he took them. By the time he left, he was starting to feel a little confused. He thought it was just the shock of being free for the first time in eighteen years. His P.O. told him it was quite common and would wear off in time.

It didn't. The confusion got worse. He walked off his job, which technically was a violation of his parole, and his P.O. could have sent him back to prison for it. But Chuckie's P.O. didn't think he was much of a criminal. He could see he was in no shape to work. He advised him to see the psychiatrist the hospital had referred him to, but Chuckie refused. There was nothing the P.O. could do about that; being confused was not a crime. He helped him apply for General Assistance so he could keep his apartment.

Chuckie got more and more confused. He doesn't remember why, but he remembers he used to follow strangers around and match his steps to theirs as though he was their shadow or something. It scared them and they would complain to the police. This behavior, though odd, wasn't a crime either. So at first the police just shooed him away. When he did it persistently for several days in a row, the police would take him to the county hospital for observation. The doctors at county hospital would pump some meds into him and in a few days he would be okay. They would lecture him to be sure to take his meds, and discharge him. He wouldn't take his meds and the whole scenario would start over again.

Each time around he got confused a little quicker, but it took longer to be forcibly detained. The downtown cops got used to him and they figured out he wasn't really dangerous. They also knew he would be back on the streets in a few days anyway. The staff at the county hospital was just as frustrated. If he refused to follow their aftercare advice, there wasn't much good a few days of hospitalization could do for him. And he didn't meet the criteria for long-term commitment because he wasn't currently a threat to himself or others, despite his history. When the police brought him in the sixth time in the eighteen months since he left the corrections facility, the hospital refused to admit him. "Charge him with a crime," they said, "then his P.O. can revoke his parole. Or else leave him alone. We can't do anything for him."

They let him go that time, but a couple of weeks later they arrested him and charged him with "lurking with intent to commit a crime." Exactly what crime was never clear, but it was enough to give his P.O. the leverage he needed. He filed for parole revocation, which got another public defender assigned. The options were back to prison for six months, or back to Mendota on a 120 day "voluntary commitment." Chuckie was inclined to choose prison, but his lawyer talked him into Mendota. By the time Chuckie arrived, Phil had finally been transferred to Mendota after twenty-four years at Shakopee, and promoted to the unlocked unit, so they were ward-mates again.

Phil was working on a discharge to something called the Fairweather Program. He seemed awfully excited about it. "It feels great to be getting out," he explained, "but freedom is a double-edged sword. Fairweather comes with a guaranteed job and guaranteed home with no pressure to move on. Those other halfway houses are only good for a certain number of months. I'm a little nervous about taking care of myself out there after all these years on the inside. It's been twenty-five years, you know."

"What about your sister's family," Chuckie asked, "couldn't you live with them?"

"She and John said I could stay with them for a while, but they've got kids and problems of their own. I'm not sure they really want me. I think I could live by myself, but I like the structure in the lodge."

The Fairweather Program was all that Phil expected and more. He quickly graduated from the training phase and moved on to the Painters Lodge. It was called the Painters Lodge because they used to paint houses for a living. Now they cleaned office buildings because it was less seasonal than painting, but they kept the name.

He was a little nervous that there wouldn't be any on-site staff in the lodge. He understood the rules and felt he could follow them without supervision, but he was worried about the other residents. He had seen plenty of goof-ball behavior and he was tired of it. He was forty-two but he felt fifty-two. He was looking for peace and quiet.

It turned out the other residents of Painters Lodge, "members" they called themselves, were pretty much like him.

Not quite the same history as his, but mature guys who "took care of business" as they called it.

Phil felt at home right away. It was a nicer house than he expected, full of the comforts he had been denied for so long, a spacious private bedroom, for example. He was sharing a bathroom with Calvin and Trevor, but both were as neat as pins. Each guy kept his stuff where it belonged. Most of the time their bathroom looked like one at the Holiday Inn. Phil loved it.

The food was good (they took turns cooking) and the work was good. Another thing he liked about the Painters Lodge was the stability. The openings he and Trevor had filled were the first they'd had in four years. Calvin had been there fifteen years.

He felt sad to think of how he had spent those years compared to how they had spent theirs, but he knew what he had done and felt thrilled to be here now. He knew he could have gotten the chair or the gas in other states.

Chuckie followed Phil to the Fairweather Training Program, but he didn't like it; too many rules. He arrived only two weeks before Phil graduated to the Lodge. Phil told Chuckie he would like Fairweather if he would relax and flow with the program, but he didn't relax and he never flowed. He quit a week after Phil left. Because his 120-day commitment was up, he told his P.O. he was leaving. His P.O. didn't tell him he couldn't, so he left.

His P.O. didn't offer to help him get a job or an apartment though. He had to do that by himself. He found one of each, but neither was great. The job didn't last and the apartment was a disaster. It was full of cockroaches and the people next door played rock music all night long.

He didn't like taking meds but he promised his P.O. that he

would. His P.O. didn't demand it; it was a voluntary promise. They both knew what would happen if he didn't. And he intended to take them, every third day or so, often enough to stay out of trouble. But he couldn't sleep nights at his hell-hole apartment. Once he lost his job, he tried to sleep days instead of nights, but that wasn't easy either. So sometimes he slept days and sometimes he slept nights and most of the time he didn't sleep at all. He found it hard to keep track which was the third day. Pretty soon he was out mimicking people on the streets again.

Right, left, right, left. Most people were easy to time, but some would get nervous and stutter-step, or change their pace to try and fool him — right, left, right, (pause) left, right, right, left. They couldn't fool him, though.

They admitted him one more time at county hospital, but even as they did they told the police it wouldn't do any good and not to bring him again. The second time the police picked him up it was about dusk. They told him they were tired of his ugly face and he should go bother people in St. Paul for a while. He remembers wondering, "How would that help?" By then it was dark. They took him into an alley and beat him up. He lay in the alley until dawn. He thought about his life. He thought about his baby sister. As the light of a new day crept over the horizon, he came up with a plan.

Phil was the only guy he could think of who might lend him money. He asked around and found the Painters Lodge. Phil wasn't in the habit of lending anyone money, but Chuckie looked so pitiful, all beat up, that he gave him $100.

"Two things," Phil said. "It's a gift not a loan, so don't worry about paying me back. And number two, don't ever ask me again."

Chuckie used the $100 to buy a pistol and handful of bullets. He went down by the river to kill himself, but when he got there he couldn't do it. He put the pistol to his head several times and tried to make himself pull the trigger, but the gun never went off. After a long time, he gave up and threw the pistol in the river.

He walked to county hospital. Even though he had come on his own, which he had never done before, they wouldn't admit him until he agreed to another voluntary commitment at Mendota. He agreed.

Once his head got straight, he started thinking about his buddy Phil, what a nice house he lived in and how easy it was to peel those twenties out of his wallet. He was ashamed of himself for having borrowed money from his only friend and then to have thrown the damned thing in the river. "If I didn't have the guts to kill myself," he thought, "the least I could have done was return the pistol and gotten most of Phil's money back." Despite what Phil had said, Chuckie was determined to repay the debt.

He thought about how much he and Phil had in common. And how Phil seemed so happy when Chuckie was so miserable. He decided to give the Fairweather Program another try.

The Fairweather Training Program was the toughest place he had ever been. He didn't mind working, but at Fairweather everything had to be perfect or this guy Ray got in your face about it. Twice he threatened to quit, and at least as often they threatened to kick him out. It was supposed to be a ninety-day training program, but it was seven months before Chuckie finally graduated to a lodge.

There weren't any openings at the Painters Lodge so he was sent to the Spirit Lodge. It took him a lot longer to get comfortable at Spirit than it had Phil at the Painters, but by the end of the first year he felt he had made the right decision.

The Painters and the Spirits had been located fairly close to each other initially, although the Painters were in a much nicer neighborhood. Then, shortly before Chuckie joined up, the Spirits moved to the suburbs, quite a distance from the Painters. When the two lodges were close, most of the guys at each lodge used the same barber shop, Joe's, about halfway between the two lodges. There was a chain-type barber shop in the mall near the new Spirit Lodge, but it had bright lights, jazzy music, and girl barbers, all of which intimidated the Spirits. So mostly they continued to patronize Joe's. Chuckie followed his lodge mates there. He liked the atmosphere and Joe cut his hair okay.

Phil was particular about his hair. Although his once thick blond hair had grown thin and grey, he still wore it in a D.A. (just as he still wore Camels in his sleeve, even though he had cut back his smoking to three or four smokes a day). After decades of bad haircuts in Shakopee, he was thrilled to discover that Joe knew how to cut a D.A. He was devoted to Joe and wouldn't go anywhere else.

Phil liked to get down to Joe's about nine a.m. so that he had plenty of time to get his haircut before starting work at eleven. He went in one day, several years after he and Chuckie had joined Fairweather. A couple of old timers, fishing buddies of Joe's whom Phil had seen before, were hanging around.

Phil walked in on the middle of an extraordinary story. Joe was a great storyteller, mostly about fishing. The story this day was about a fellow whose hair Joe had cut the day before and several times before that; Joe didn't know his name. This fellow had been in the chair while another customer was describing his new son-in-law, who happened to be a parole officer.

"So the feller speaks right up and says, 'I got one.'"

" 'Got one what?' I says."

" 'A parole officer' he says."

" 'Well,' I says, 'how long is youse on parole?' "

" 'For life!' he says."

" 'By golly, son, what'd you do?' I says."

" Well, he hesitates at first and then he says, 'I killed my stepmother and my baby sister.' "

"By Gott, you coulda heard a pin drop, I'm telling you. No one says a thing. Then after while the feller says, 'Of course that was a long time ago. I was in prison for years.' "

"Old Gus is here, so he says, 'So, was that around here then?' "

" 'Oh no,' the feller says, 'it was in Spicer.' "

" 'By Gott, I think I remember that,' Gus says, 'you beat 'em to a bloody pulp with a fireplace poker did ya?' "

" 'No, that was my buddy,' he says. 'I shot 'em.' "

" 'So' I says, I'm still cuttin' his hair see, 'You shot 'em before or after your buddy beat 'em with the poker then?'"

" 'No, no,' he says. 'He killed HIS stepmother with a poker, not mine. And his aunt too. That was a whole separate deal four years earlier.' "

"Well, I tell you I didn't know what to say. So after a while Gus says, 'So what about your buddy? What ever happened to him, then?' "

" 'Well,' the feller says, 'he lives around here too. Gets his hair cut right here. I know he does.' "

"Well I was finished with his hair, don't you see, so I dusted him off and he paid and left. So me and Gus, we jes looked at each other for a while. And then we broke out laughing! Gus laughed so hard I thought he was gonna wet his pants. Imagine a feller coming in here and spinning a tale like that and us almost falling for it."

"I just remember something I gotta do before work," Phil said as he bolted out of the shop. "I'll be back tomorrow."

He called Chuckie that evening to tell him a thing or two. One of the things was, don't ever go back to Joe's. "Joe is MY barber. You're not allowed to go there and I mean it!"

The other thing was that if Chuckie wanted to tell the world what he had done when he was sixteen, that was his business. "But don't go talking about me. You don't know what went on in my house. It wasn't the same as what you did."

> *"I remember there was a time in my life when I couldn't do anything. I don't remember why."*
>
> **Judy Louise Fortier**
> **Lilac and Hiawatha Lodges**

CHAPTER THREE

HELPLESS IN DULUTH

"I'm here," she announced.

Ray looked up from his paperwork to see a woman standing in the doorway. She was a tall, broad-shouldered, fortyish woman with light brown hair and a medium build. She spoke as though he was expecting her, but his mind was blank.

"My things are in the cab," she said, her speech bursting with unexplained urgency.

Ray stretched his neck to see around the file cabinet and out to the street. Sure enough, there was a taxi. The driver was unloading bags.

"Are you ...you must be...," he searched for a name, "...the new client?"

She ignored his question. "Can you show me my room and get someone to carry in my things?"

"Sure; in a second. I'm Ray. What's your name?"

"Judy Louise Fortier, " she said.

"Right, right, nice to meet you, Judy. Everyone is eating lunch, but I can help you with your bags."

She stepped aside to let him pass, but she made no move to follow him as he walked out the front door toward the taxi. The driver had assembled an enormous pile of baggage on the sidewalk.

"Is this stuff all ... ?" he started to ask as he glanced over his shoulder and realized she wasn't there. He could not tell from the reflected glare whether she was in the front hall or his office.

Ray picked up the two closest suitcases. He carried them up the three porch steps, set one down, opened the door and held it with his foot while he picked it up again and carried both bags into the hall. Judy watched from the office door.

"We don't offer bellhop service," he said a grin. "You'll have to help me with this."

"I can't lift them, " she said, not changing her expression.

Ray shrugged and thought, "Great, the first two were the only light ones," as he headed back to the taxi.

The next two bags Ray picked up were lighter than the first two. "That's odd," he thought. He set them down and picked up two different ones. One was medium heavy and the other very light, almost as though it were empty. He carried these two into the house, opening the door with the hand which held the light suitcase. Judy was still watching.

"These aren't all heavy," he said, "surely you can lift some of them."

"I have bad ankles," she said.

Reflexively, he looked down at her ankles, but there was nothing to see as the bottom of her slacks touched the tops of her shoes. He took another look at the still huge pile of baggage by the taxi and went to the dining room to recruit some help. As he and two male clients carried Judy's luggage, Ray thought to himself, "I gotta read the charts closer, I missed the part about her ankles. I wonder if it will prevent her from working?"

By the time Ray and his helpers had piled all of Judy's luggage into her room, which was completely filled by it, lunch was over. "Have you eaten?" Ray asked.

"No."

He led her to the kitchen and checked for leftovers, but there weren't any. He pulled a loaf of bread and a jar of peanut butter out of the pantry. He set a plate, a knife, and a glass on the counter next to them. "You'll have to make yourself a peanut butter sandwich. There's milk and juice in the 'fridge. There's a group meeting in twenty minutes and I'll introduce you to everybody then."

He turned to leave the kitchen, but stopped when she asked, "Who is going to make the sandwich?"

"You'll have to do it yourself," he answered. "The clients do all the cooking here, and the lunch crew has already cleaned up."

"I don't know how to make a sandwich."

Ray had worked with dysfunctional people for over ten years and thought he'd heard everything, but he was stunned. While he fumbled for a response, his mind raced back to the admission chart he had read a week ago.

"Wasn't this the woman who is a college graduate?" he thought to himself. "Or am I confusing her with someone else?"

Judy was a college graduate, St. Scholastica in Duluth. She had a diploma and a certified transcript to prove it. It is a good thing she kept the documents because Judy has little memory of her college days.

She remembers, with the assistance of medical records, being hospitalized twice for schizo-affective disorder during college. She remembers Sister Mary-Something, who helped her study for her final exams. In her wallet she carries a picture of herself in a cap and gown, but she has no actual recollection of the ceremony. She remembers, again with assistance, a third lengthy hospitalization beginning one week after graduation.

This sort of memory loss is common among people treated extensively with Electro-Convulsive Therapy (ECT). Her records were incomplete, so a verified total is impossible, but Judy claimed, when she arrived at the Lodge Training Program, to have received over 120 ECT treatments.

Judy was, still is, convinced that ECT was the cause of her illness rather than an attempted cure. She believes the five different doctors who administered the ECT conspired to "keep me crazy," each doc covering for the crimes of the previous one. When she caught on to the plot and threatened to sue, the last of the conspirators administered a "triple dose of ECT designed to shut me up."

What is verifiable is that following her graduation from St. Scholastica, Judy lived the next sixteen years of her life in nursing homes. For years in Duluth, she was the only young person in a home serving elderly people. After relocating to Minneapolis (she doesn't remember why and her records don't say), she lived in nursing homes which included other young psychiatric patients among their residents.

The notable events of those sixteen years, at least as documented in her records, were a series of self-inflicted cuts and punctures, none of which were life threatening. Judy remembers being stitched up on several occasions, but doesn't remember why she would have cut herself.

Besides multiple doctors, Judy was treated by various psychotherapists. She remembers one in particular, who maintained that her illness was the result of childhood sexual abuse, probably by her father. Judy's father died when she was in high school. She has very little memory of him. She has a picture of him and she remembers that while in therapy she used to stare at the picture for hours, trying to remember what he did to her. It didn't help.

A subsequent therapist recommended her for an apartment training program. She took a series of classes designed to train her for independent living. There were tests in each skill area which the students were supposed to pass before getting an apartment. Judy remembers flunking every test.

Nevertheless, she was given an opportunity to live in her own apartment. With the assistance of a staff member from the apartment program, Judy picked out an apartment. With staff help and a special grant, she shopped for furniture and household items to stock the apartment. Counting the training classes, Judy had spent over a year preparing for life in her own apartment. She was very excited the day she moved in.

The excitement generated enough adrenaline to carry Judy through the first full day. By the third day, she decided that living independently was terribly strenuous. Despite her training, and even with the assistance of the staff who visited daily, feeding herself and cleaning up afterwards was an overwhelming task.

The elevator was another problem. The doors would not open immediately when she pushed the button. Exhausted as she was, Judy found it necessary to sit down while waiting. The apartment management had not provided chairs for this purpose, so Judy would sit on the floor opposite the elevator. Although the elevator was slow to respond it was very quick, in Judy's opinion, to open and shut. Before she could get up and into the elevator, it was gone again. Judy found the only way she could catch the elevator was to sit immediately in front of the doors and crawl into the elevator when they opened. After she did this a couple of times in the lobby, other tenants complained.

Judy's career as an apartment dweller lasted less than one week. Several months later she was referred to Tasks Unlimited.

Judy was an enigma to Ray. She had a degree in Home Economics, but she couldn't cook; she couldn't do laundry; she couldn't make her bed. Although her hygiene was generally good (she didn't need the encouragement to shower that many lodge trainees needed), she asked for help each day to wash her hair.

Her second day at the Lodge Training Center, Ray asked her to set the dining room table for nine people.

"I don't know how," Judy said.

"Which part don't you know how?" Ray asked.

"I've never done it before."

"Yes, but which part don't you know how?"

"I don't know where to get stuff."

"In the cupboards, I'll show you,"

"I don't know where to put it."

"Everybody gets one plate, one glass, one fork. Like that."

"I don't know which side the fork goes on."

"Technically the left, but it doesn't matter."

"There's twelve chairs. How do I know where the nine people will want to sit?"

"They'll sit wherever you put the plates."

"Gee, I don't know."

"You can do this."

"Maybe I should watch somebody else do it for a couple of weeks."

The Lodge Training Program also included a vocational component. Trainees were assigned to perform janitorial work on a special crew. They worked in a real office setting where the customer expected a clean building each morning, but the crew was staffed at a level to accommodate inexperienced workers.

Judy tried several assignments during her first few weeks,

but didn't like any of them. Her main complaint about janitorial work was that it required her to be on her feet.

At 155 pounds, Judy was maybe ten to twenty pounds overweight for a five foot eight inch woman, but she had convinced herself that she was obese, barely able to walk. Although her weight was relatively stable, she imagined herself getting heavier and heavier until she could not walk at all, like a woman she had read about in a magazine.

She had also obtained, from a nursing home doctor (apparently after persistent badgering), a diagnosis of mild arthritis related to the loss of flexibility which naturally occurs with age. Judy's joints were not as flexible as they had been at age seventeen, but they were fairly normal for a woman of thirty-seven. Nevertheless, she had inflated the arthritis into a tragic and degenerative condition. She truly believed she could not walk and stand for more than a few minutes at a time.

In addition to the largely imaginary physical problems, Judy's confidence level was extraordinarily low. There were some things that she knew how to do. She had acquired a few basic craft and sewing skills during her nursing home experiences, for example. But everything else was beyond her. If she had not done something recently, she couldn't do it. Even skills she must surely have learned as an adolescent now eluded her.

From time to time Judy had been encouraged to volunteer for certain jobs around the nursing home. She tried folding towels in the laundry, answering phones, and elementary bookkeeping, but it was all too difficult. She enjoyed serving as the "library cart lady" one day a week, but she gave it up when she discovered she had arthritis.

Judy's initiation to janitorial training was a struggle for everyone involved, even the other trainees. In the van on the way to work the first day, she repeatedly explained to Ray that she didn't know how.

"I've never done janitorial. I don't know how. This isn't going to work; I've already forgotten what I am supposed to do first."

Ray started to answer, "As I just told you a minute ago..."

"I know, I know you told me," Judy interrupted, "I already forgot. That's why I can't..."

"What I told you was..."

"I know, I'm sorry, I'm really trying..."

"What I said was..."

"I'm sorry, I didn't know I'd be expected to..."

"I'll explain it when we get there."

"What?"

"What you are supposed to do."

"I forgot already. That's what I'm trying to tell you."

"You forgot because I haven't told you..., what I mean is, you can't have forgotten because..."

"It's the ECT. I can't remember anything since the ECT."

"You can't remember because I haven't told you yet."

"What?"

"I haven't told you what to do yet. I'll show you what to do when we get there."

"I don't think I can do this."

There were three chairs in the janitorial training office. Ray took the one behind the desk. Judy took one of the other chairs.

The third stayed empty as the other trainees milled around waiting for assignments and snickering to one another about Judy. Her anxiety seemed to subside as Ray made assignments and the other trainees gathered their supplies and left. Ray noticed and thought to himself that the calm demeanor of the other trainees was helping to convince Judy that things would be okay.

As was standard procedure, Ray saved the last assignment for the newest trainee, so that he could go over it step by step.

He assigned Judy to a small vacuuming route. (Vacuuming was the least complicated of all janitorial skills.) He selected a vacuum he was certain was in good working order and extended the handle to Judy. "Take this, and follow me down the hall."

"I can't do this. I don't know how."

"You can't take it, or you can't follow me?"

"I can't vacuum. I don't know how."

"This is a training program. It's my job to teach you how. I'll show you how when we get to 103."

"How far is it?"

"I've only assigned you a short route to start with. If you finish before break ... Oh, you mean how far is it to room 103? It's not far. We can walk there from here."

He led Judy to 103. Ray plugged the vacuum in, turned it on, and demonstrated proper vacuuming technique. He stressed the importance of moving small items such as chairs and waste-baskets to vacuum under them. He told Judy not to try to move desks, or file cabinets. He told her not to worry about the last half inch along the wall, or heavy furniture, except for visible litter which she should pick up by hand. Warren, a more experienced trainee, would come by once a week with a special edging tool.

He asked Judy to vacuum 103, followed by the numberless room behind 103, followed by room 105 across the hall.

"Do I have to do all of that today?" asked Judy.

"Uh, yes, it shouldn't take more than fifteen minutes. I'll be back before ..."

"Because I'm tired already."

"You haven't started yet."

"Doesn't this count? We've been standing here forever."

"Well, yes, you're on the clock already. But ..."

"I'm being timed?"

"No, it means that you're being paid."

"How much?"

"Not much yet. You're going to have to do something first. By the time you graduate I expect you to be able to vacuum the entire first floor of this building."

"How many weeks will that take?"

"No, I mean daily."

"In one day?"

"Before the first break."

Ray switched the machine on and put the handle in Judy's hand. He watched for a minute as Judy pushed the vacuum back and forth. Her technique was pretty good and Ray told her so. Confident that she would be okay for a few minutes, Ray hurried down the hall to check on Chris, who was working bathrooms with John for the first time.

The "Restroom Closed" sign was leaning against the door inside the doorway. Ray moved it to the hall in front of the doorway where it was supposed to be. As he started into the bathroom, he called out "How is it going?"

As he did, he heard Judy's voice behind him. "I broke it. I'm really sorry."

Ray turned around, "You broke what?"

"That big thing. I can't remember what it's called, but I broke it. I'm really sorry. I knew I couldn't do this."

Ray was semi-stunned as they walked back down the hall. He tried to visualize the breakable items in 103, "The desk lamp? The picture on the wall? Oh, god, not the computer ..."

Judy continued to apologize and explained that she didn't know how she broke it, it just broke.

Ray surveyed the scene. With a sigh of relief, he explained to Judy, "This 'big thing' is called a vacuum cleaner, and it isn't really broken. You seem to have inadvertently switched it off."

Over time, Judy became more comfortable with the operational features of the vacuum. The quality of her work was surprisingly good. If she said she was through with a room, Ray knew the carpet was clean. She was slow, however, to accept the physical demands of a vacuuming route. Many of the offices she was assigned to vacuum contained desk chairs with wheels. When Ray wasn't watching, Judy would vacuum the office sitting down.

Ray discussed Judy's physical condition with the other training staff. The physical exam she had in preparation for admission to Tasks was clean, no restrictions. The problems with her ankles and her stamina seemed entirely somatic. They adopted a strategy of not discussing Judy's physical problems with her.

The initial expectations of Judy were reduced far below normal for a new trainee, but very gradually they were raised. When something new was added Judy would insist she didn't know how. Staff would explain, some more patiently than others, exactly how to do it. Over time, they discovered it was unnecessary to explain things more than once. Judy's short term memory was good, and once she practiced a skill, she seemed to retain it.

"I don't know how," was frequently followed by, "it's too hard," or "my ankles hurt," or most frequently, "I'm too tired."

Eventually all staff adopted a consistent response, "Hmmm, well, you'll have to do it. It's your responsibility."

Judy quickly caught on that the training staff were plotting against her. She objected to this manipulative and humiliating treatment. Her objections were assertive, well reasoned, and passionately presented. They were also in vain. Staff refused to discuss her physical problems and continued to raise expectations.

By the end of her second month in training, Judy's productivity, both around the house and at the worksite, matched that of a typical new admission. Her quality remained excellent.

By the fourth month, Judy was progressing nicely toward graduation. She had been assigned, and grudgingly accepted, the responsibility of Medication Witness. That is, she was responsible for observing the other trainees as they took their medications, and recording what was taken or not taken.

When Judy graduated, she chose the all female Lilac Lodge. The Lilacs had a reputation as the low-skilled lodge, at least at work. They had the least demanding job responsibilities, for which they were paid minimum wage, far less than some of the other lodges. They were held to the same lodge maintenance standards as other lodges, but they had a smaller home and a smaller yard to take care of.

Transition from the heavily staffed training program to an unstaffed lodge is often a difficult adjustment, but much to everyone's surprise, Judy adjusted well. Initially she suckered a couple of the more gullible Lilacs into doing things for her she could have done for herself, but the Lilacs caught on quickly. Before very long, Judy was carrying a normal load of responsibility.

The Tasks social worker, Darcy, who had been briefed by Ray, was amazed. Once convinced the changes in Judy were real, Darcy began to promote Judy as a candidate for various leadership responsibilities. Judy was the only college graduate at the Lilacs, and they were impressed with her verbal skills. By the end of the first year, she was considered to be co-leader of the group, along with Jo Ellen, the official Chair.

Towards the end of the second year, Darcy noticed that Judy's growth spurt had slowed. She was functioning at a higher level than she ever had in her adult life, but she had re-acquired the old habit of refusing to try new things. Darcy suggested to Judy that she consider transferring to another lodge, Hiawatha. Judy was doubly mortified; she assumed she had done something wrong and was being rejected by the Lilacs; and she could not imagine herself keeping up with the energetic gang at the Hiawatha Lodge.

Darcy asked Judy to think about it. She brought it up a month later and Judy still said no. A month later the same thing. The fourth month, Judy asked Darcy to explain again why she should move. But she still rejected the idea of moving.

The following month Darcy didn't bring it up. At the end of their meeting Judy asked, "Aren't you going to ask me about moving?"

"Do you want to move?"

"No," Judy said.

"Then why should I ask you?"

"You always do."

"Do you want me to ask you?"

"Isn't it your job?"

"Yeah ... well ... not specifically."

"Do you still think I should move?"

"I think it would be good for you."

"Then you ought to ask me."

"It's a waste of time if you always say no."

"My half hour is not up."

"What half hour?"

"I'm supposed to get a full half hour of your time each month."

"Who told you that?"

"Everybody else around here gets a half an hour."

"No, they don't, " protested Darcy. "Some get more and some get less. It depends on what you need."

"I need a half an hour."

"To ask you the same question over and over?"

"If you think I should move, it's your job to keep asking me."

"Do you want me to ask you again right now in case you've changed your mind in the last two minutes?"

"My half hour is not up."

"Do you want to move to the Hiawatha Lodge where the expectations are higher and you can continue to grow?"

"I guess so."

Judy's transition to the Hiawatha Lodge was a little rocky, especially at work. Although the Hiawathans and Lilacs worked together cleaning the courthouse, the building was, by tradition, considered the Hiawathan's contract. Everett was in charge and he assigned all the heavy work to the men of Hiawatha. He also expected more from the women of Hiawatha than from the Lilacs. In the same four-hour shift, Judy was now expected to vacuum, dust and trash a larger area than she needed only to vacuum when working with the Lilacs. Everett gave her a little time to get up to speed, but not enough in Judy's opinion.

Another problem was that Judy had gotten into the habit of bossing the Lilac Lodge around. The Lilacs didn't seem to mind. The men at the Hiawatha Lodge minded a lot. To make matters worse, Hiawathans Sandi and Lois were excellent cooks. Judy's rudimentary cooking skills were a major disappointment by this unspoken standard.

Judy was ready to give up, and requested a transfer back to the Lilac Lodge. Darcy stalled, hoping for a miracle; and she got one.

Everett's brother, Ed, tore his brand new jeans. Ed was very upset. He not only didn't know how to repair them, it didn't even occur to him that it was possible. He was ready to throw them away. Judy, who had sewn quite a bit while at the Lilacs, offered to attempt the repair. When she was finished, Ed thought the jeans were better than new.

Judy was soon very popular at the Hiawatha Lodge. She would mend and sew on buttons for whoever asked her, mostly the men. In return, the men of the Hiawatha Lodge helped her out at work.

Judy never became a leader of the Hiawatha Lodge, but she lived there quite happily for four and a half years. Then she applied for and was accepted into the part of the Tasks program in which she could live in her own apartment downtown, but continue to work with the Hiawatha Lodge.

Judy was very excited about getting her own apartment. She remembered her earlier failure with more amusement than fear. She felt that she was much better prepared this time around. Not only was Judy's energy level dramatically higher, her cooking and cleaning skills were good enough to get by. Her biggest problem in adjusting to her own apartment was being alone. Judy had never been alone before. She thought she was going to love it, but when the Hiawathans who helped her move all went home and she shut her door, the apartment seemed a little spooky.

Judy tried to make friends with her neighbors. The elderly people seemed afraid of her; they didn't want to be friends. The younger people were disabled, as she knew she was, but she found she had little in common with them.

Some were mentally ill, but unlike Judy and the people that she had lived with in the lodge, they weren't taking their medications consistently. They would be perfectly pleasant one day, and completely off the wall the next. Judy found them a little scary. Even scarier were Judy's neighbors on drugs. Not the good kind, the bad kind.

Judy discussed her loneliness with Darcy. Darcy gave her ideas, but they didn't seem to help. Eventually Darcy asked Judy if she wanted to move back to the Hiawatha Lodge.

Judy said, "No, but ask me again next month."

"How about working full time? You'd have less time to sit here by yourself. And maybe you could earn enough to get a real apartment outside of public housing."

"No way. Absolutely not. You don't need to even ask me again."

"Hey, it's my job. Think about it."

Darcy returned the next month assuming that Judy would still be lonely. She planned to bring up (not push, just bring up) both the lodge option and the full time work.

It turned out Judy had solved the problem on her own.

"You remember me talking abut Holy Cross Nursing Home? The one I was in before the one before I came to Tasks? Where I learned how to do all those crafts? I signed up to be a volunteer craft instructor. Three mornings a week, before I go to work. They're understaffed and they really appreciate my help. A lot of the patients just sit around all day not doing anything and we've gotta get 'em moving. If I can get them interested in crafts, maybe they could get a job someday."

*"I think I was there for some
symbolic function."*

Keith Swanstrom
County Social Worker

CHAPTER FOUR

WHEN HARVEY
MET SANDI

She stood in the doorway, swaying her hips and her shoulders
in an almost hypnotic pattern. Although the sun was pouring
in the window opposite the door, throwing her shadow into the
hallway, her rhythm somehow radiated back into the room,
stirring Harvey's blood. Before he noticed her standing there,
the juices in Harvey's body began to pulse. Music he didn't
recognize came from nowhere.

Most of all, Harvey's jaw started to move, ever so slightly
at first, and then more noticeably, the powerful muscle which
attached his jaw to his skull twitching in a strange rhythm,
syncopating with the unseen stranger swaying in the doorway.

Harvey had never experienced this sense of motion before,
but he had seen plenty of involuntary motion in Mendota.
Extrapyramidal side effects, the doctors called it; "can't be
helped," they said. Harvey knew it second hand as the Prolixin

Shuffle. But he had never taken Prolixin and this rhythm he suddenly felt wasn't unpleasant. It was warm and exhilarating.

"Hello," she said.

Harvey jumped at the sound, and spun away from the suitcase he had been unpacking. Swaying in the doorway was a striking woman. She had a strong healthy figure, soft penetrating eyes and dark blonde hair. But it was her sway that paralyzed Harvey.

Usually glib, he felt overpowered by the rhythm of her swaying. He tried to say something clever to this astonishing woman, but the words which came out made no sense, "How are I'd known..."

"You must be the new guy," she said.

Harvey was the new guy. He had made a career of being the new guy.

Since his first foster home at age fourteen, Harvey had been on the move. A few months in the hospital, a few months on the street, always moving. A little day labor here and there, occasionally a real job, but rarely past the second pay check.

The longest job he ever had was at a music store. When the manager realized that the weird-looking drifter he had hired to help unload a truck knew more about classical music than he did, he put Harvey on the payroll as a stockboy. When the owner discovered the new stockboy knew how to repair stringed instruments and had a huge chip on his shoulder, he decided Harvey was an artist.

The owner set up a workshop in the back of the store, and let him sleep there too. He put Harvey on commission repairing instruments. The owner praised his repair skills and predicted they would both become rich off the business. But Harvey began to suspect that many of the violins he repaired had been damaged deliberately by youngsters who were not nearly as interested in classical music as their parents. He began pointing this out to the customers, rebuking the youngsters regarding their obligation to respect their instruments, and the parents regarding the inadequacy of their parenting skills. After repeated complaints from ungrateful parents, Harvey and the music store parted company.

The most attached he had ever been to any one place or thing was to the Ranch. The Ranch was a drop-in center he hung around at when he wasn't in the hospital. It started off as a drop-in center. Harvey's idea of a real "drop-in" was where everyone was welcome, all the time. The Ranch was actually open only from 6 p.m. to 2 a.m., but Harvey wasn't a morning person anyway. And it was open 365 days a year.

The name "Ranch" was a joke nickname that everybody used, even the staff. Some hippie social worker opened the place in an old warehouse downtown, about as un-ranchlike as could be. According to legend, the founder intended the drop-in to serve people like himself, middle-class types who had chosen to be poor. It didn't turn out that way. No sooner had the place opened in the summer of 1970 than it was overrun by a mentally ill clientele. It took a long time, however, for the founder and his hippie friends to figure this out. The downsizing of state institutions had only just begun, and the general public had not yet caught on to the fact that highly institutionalized patients were being discharged to the streets without follow-up services.

Although the Ranch's hippie staff did not recognize schizophrenia when they saw it, they did notice that their clientele was a little odd, and slightly dysfunctional. Looking for a pattern, they began to ask people where they were from. Some said they were born in Ohio, or wherever, but most named the state hospital they had spent most of their adult lives in; referring to it by the community where it was located, as in "I'm from Fergus Falls," "I'm from Moose Lake," or "I'm from Willmar." All were small towns (a product of the "pastoral therapy" movement). The hippies, unfamiliar with the Minnesota state hospital system, mistakenly identified these towns as being in western Minnesota, *i.e.*, out on the prairie. They hypothesized that the dysfunction was the result of the difficulty unsophisticated "ranch hands" were having adjusting to the big city. They began asking newcomers if they were from a ranch. Most of people, mistaking the question for an admission criterion, went along. Hence the nickname.

Later, when the hippies had all gone off to graduate school or the suburbs, the city took responsibility for operating the Ranch. The city hired social workers who recognized mental illness and knew what people with mental illness needed. They changed the hours to noon to 8 p.m., Monday through Friday, and designed admission forms to document that everyone was eligible for city services. So, no one Harvey knows ever goes there anymore.

But he used to hang out there quite a bit; the atmosphere of chaos and tension kind of appealed to him. He had some wild times there. It was the closest thing he had to a home.

Other people were the force which kept Harvey moving. They were always the cause of Harvey getting locked up or hospitalized, always the cause of moving on. Harvey would make friends with a guy who had an apartment and wangle an invitation to stay a couple of nights. A couple of nights would turn into a month and things would be looking up. Then there would be a problem. With the guy, the guy's girlfriend, maybe the landlord. Soon Harvey would be on the street again.

Harvey hadn't expected the lodge to last any longer, a few months at most. The most recent hospital he had been a patient in sent him to a residential program where they "trained" him to be a janitor. Except Harvey had swung a lot of mops over the years and knew more about janitorial work than Ray the Trainer, and he let him know it. He also knew more about art, history, science, and literature than Ray did, and much more about mental illness. He let him know that too.

It was a weird program. They had a ton of rules. Every time Ray caught you breaking one he was on your case about it. You could break the same rule every day for a week, and every day Ray would act surprised and make a big deal about it. Being late for breakfast was like you just killed somebody. And if you went a whole day without breaking a rule, at least without getting caught, Ray would make something up just to have an excuse to get on your case.

The frustrating part for Harvey was that Ray wouldn't hassle him in person so he could fight back. When Ray caught, or imagined, him breaking a rule, he would write a note about it and put it in a box. Once each day the trainees would meet without staff to review the notes. The group chair, *i.e.*, a trainee gullible enough to think staff would go easy on him if he played their game, would read the notes aloud. Then everyone would discuss the notes.

Harvey would get a note for something moronic, like not rearranging the chairs properly after cleaning the dining room. Harvey would explain the fallacy of trying to apply eighteenth century bourgeois dining customs to a seven-minute chow-down at the funny farm. No one would say anything for a while, and then Alan, the semi-literate chairman would explain that when he had dining room duty, he used the pattern in the wallpaper as a guide to get the chairs lined up straight. In the end, Harvey would get stuck with a demerit.

He was as street smart as he was well read, and part of being street smart is knowing how to beat other people at their own games. He quickly got himself elected chair, and from then on the notes written about him got thrown out on some technicality or other. Sometimes Ray would appeal the training group's decision to let Harvey off the hook, but the rules had been written in a way which allowed the "inmates (*i.e.*, the trainees) to rule the asylum." Harvey thought it was an incredibly dumb system, but one which worked to his advantage.

Before long, he graduated to the lodge. He assumed the lodge would be a new game, which he could play for a while and move on. He wasn't counting on the swaying blonde.

Her name was Sandi. She was from a farm in southern Minnesota. Except for her schizophrenia and her peculiar swaying motion, she was the classic midwestern farmer's daughter: strong, smart, kind, hardworking, and confident.

Right after high school, Sandi married a much older man. Three years later, when she caught him with another woman, she divorced him without a second thought. She moved to the cities and got by on her own for a while. But then her illness struck; she was hospitalized twice, six months the first time and almost a year the second time. While she was in the hospital the second time, her landlord sold off all her clothes and furniture to cover what she owed on the lease. And she lost her job.

She told the nurse at the hospital that working was important to her, so they put her in the Fairweather Training Program and discharged her to the Hiawatha Lodge. She had been there three years when Harvey moved in. The other men at Hiawatha interested Sandi, but not much. She had dated Phil and Calvin from the Painters Lodge, but neither relationship was going anywhere.

Harvey was different from the rest. Smarter, for one thing. The words he used made her head spin. When Harvey used a word that Alex, the Hiawatha Lodge Coordinator, didn't know, Alex would make him define it. And Harvey always could. He would define the word precisely and explain why he used this word and why an easier word wouldn't convey his meaning as well. It was as if he had a dictionary in his head. Alex thought Harvey was a smart ass, but Sandi thought he was the most amazing thing she'd ever seen.

Sandi was even more impressed by Harvey's knowledge of the Bible. He knew the Bible better than the dictionary, and could quote passages word for word. Once Dale thought he caught Harvey in error on a passage from Leviticus, but Harvey pointed out that Dale was looking at a revised standard version whereas Harvey was quoting the King James. Sure enough, when somebody produced a King James, the passage was word for word what Harvey said it would be. Sandi knew her mother would be impressed by a man who knew the Bible.

Harvey's knowledge of biblical sins did not prevent him from wanting to know Sandi in the biblical sense. Though less skilled than he in quoting the bible, Sandi was more inclined to take its teaching to heart. She considered knowledge of the kind Harvey had in mind to be a sacred act, reserved for the marriage contract.

An additional barrier to Harvey's plans was that the Hiawatha Lodge had a rule, supposedly made by the founding members of the lodge, prohibiting sex between members. And the Hiawatha Lodge Coordinator, Alex, was always snooping around. Actually, he wasn't around more than a few hours a week, but when he was around, he was snooping. Ineffectively, for the most part. For example, Alex was the last to know that Harvey and Sandi had taken to slipping down to the lake with a blanket after work a couple of nights a week. Exactly what they did on or under the blanket was a topic of much speculation among the other Hiawathans.

Alex probably suspected, but he didn't say anything until Harvey gave Sandi a large box of candy. Harvey gave it to her on the weekend when Alex wasn't around. Sandi was so proud of it that she didn't eat any of the candy herself but kept offering it to the other Hiawathans. She left it on the dining room buffet where Alex saw it.

It didn't take Alex two guesses to figure out who gave the candy to whom. He asked to speak to the two of them privately. Sandi admitted receiving the candy from Harvey. Harvey said he loved Sandi and that there weren't any rules against love or gift giving. Alex referred to the rule against sex. Harvey refused to admit or deny anything, but pointed out that the candy was not incriminating as to intercourse having actually occurred.

Alex took the position that even if they had not yet had sex, they would soon enough; expensive presents lead in that direction. He said it was not normal or healthy to date someone who was essentially your roommate. Furthermore, in Alex's opinion, their relationship was already having a negative impact on the lodge. Just last week, Dale had complained about Sandi holding up the whole group when they were leaving for work. Harvey had gone ballistic in her defense, pointing out (correctly, but more vociferously than necessary) that they got to work on time, and that Dale's complaint was ridiculous. Other Hiawathans found Sandi occasionally annoying, but no one wanted to challenge Harvey.

Harvey was ready to argue each and every point with Alex. Presents don't necessarily lead to sex; "normal" is a vague and abstract concept which cannot be employed in the evaluation of one's behavior without contamination by racist, sexist and classist values; dating a roommate is not a health issue; Dale was a moron; and if everyone except Sandi got into the van five minutes earlier than really necessary, whose problem was it?

But before Harvey could get fully wound up, Alex cut him off with a practical suggestion. It seemed there was an opening at the Painters Lodge. The Painters was a men's lodge. It was located on the other side of downtown from Hiawatha Lodge, but conveniently both lodges were on the same bus line. Alex proposed that Harvey apply for the opening at the Painters. If accepted, Harvey could continue his relationship with Sandi without breaking any rules.

Harvey's instinct had always been to reject any and all suggestion that his behavior conform to anyone else's expectations, or that his plans change for anyone else's convenience. Except when the authorities took the trouble to gather enough information to lock him up, Harvey's historical response to anyone suggesting he change his behavior had been to move on. Nobody could tell him what to do, certainly not Alex.

Sandi was another matter. Harvey found himself in love with Sandi. Not "love" as in "making love" or "I love sweet corn," but the real thing: the "love" romantic poets wrote sonnets about. He had read enough serious literature to be convinced that love really existed, but he had figured it was rare, nothing which he would ever experience. The way she swayed when she walked, when she stood, even when she sat at the kitchen table playing cribbage, drove him absolutely wild. He couldn't get enough of it. Watching Sandi empty a wastebasket at work was like foreplay. Although he was pushing forty, Harvey was in a constant state of arousal when Sandi was around. He felt the way he had as a teenager in class on a spring day; the teacher was talking isosceles triangles, but Harvey was thinking about the girl across the aisle.

It was more, though, than the way she turned him on. For reasons Harvey could not explain, he had developed this incredible pride in every thing she did. He had always been quick to point out his superior knowledge over the weirdos and transients who formed most of his social network, but he had never felt much pride about it. He was simply smarter and better read than they were, so what? Yet somehow, everything that Sandi did had become an accomplishment of Harvey's. And Sandi accomplished amazing things.

Everyone in the lodge program knew how to tie a plastic liner on a wastebasket, but nobody could tie one as tight as Sandi could. And what a cook. Sandi made old-fashioned meals like pot roast, meat loaf and homemade bread, but she could also make a quiche or a salad. Whatever she made, it came out perfect.

Sandi cooked once a week. Harvey would start talking about how wonderful the food looked before it even reached the table. Harvey would take a huge portion but would be so busy praising the meal that he barely had time to eat. He might still have a full plate when the rest of the Hiawathans were finished and ready to leave the table, but Harvey wouldn't allow anyone to leave until they had praised Sandi's cooking. Sometimes people would grunt "Good dinner, Sandi" as they got up, but Harvey would bully them into more detailed or effusive compliments before they got out of the room.

Even more amazing to Harvey was that the other male Hiawathans seemed not to notice Sandi's constant and enchanting motion. (At first Harvey suspected that Dale or maybe Everett, who was the crew chief at work, was getting it on with Sandi, and just pretended not to notice her to deceive Alex. As he got to know them better, he realized that Dale and Everett treated Sandi like a sister. She could have stripped naked in front of them and they wouldn't have noticed unless she was blocking the television.) They were all so accustomed to Sandi's swaying that no one noticed.

The idea of living apart from Sandi was initially anathema to Harvey. But Alex's plan and Sandi's quick endorsement of it caught Harvey off guard. Instead of forcefully rejecting the idea, he found himself saying he needed time to think it over. That night after work, Harvey and Sandi ate at a little Chinese restau-

rant near the lodge, a favorite strategy of theirs on the nights
Dale cooked. Harvey surprised himself as much as Sandi by
asking her to marry him. Sandi said "Yes, but not right away."

Sandi had married hastily the first time to escape the farm,
and she did not wish to repeat the mistake. Besides that, she
trusted Alex enough to know that he had her interests at heart.
She could see Harvey every weekend and once in a while during
the week. That would be often enough to sustain Harvey's interest if he really felt about her the way he said he did.

Within a week, Harvey was living at the Painters Lodge. He
looked at the move as yet another game he had to play to win
the woman he loved, but again he was pleasantly surprised. The
Painters turned out to be the hardest working, hardest laughing
guys he had ever known, and the fourteen months he spent
there were among the best times he had ever had. Harvey hadn't
bonded much with anybody, male or female, before the lodge.

Harvey had bargained a wedding date from Sandi before
agreeing to move to the Painters. She wanted a spring wedding
which was fine with Harvey because spring was just around the
corner, but she meant the following spring. Harvey didn't want
to wait fourteen months, but it was the best deal he could make.
With the camaraderie at the Painters, the months went by like
weeks.

The Hiawathans earned their living cleaning the County
Courthouse. There were many other government functions
which took place in the courthouse, but Sandi's assignment was
cleaning actual courtrooms and the judges' chambers. Over the
years, she made friends with several of the judges, especially
Judge Anderson.

Besides being a judge, Judge Anderson was also a Lutheran
minister. Sandi asked Judge Anderson to perform the ceremony

in his chambers. The wedding itself was small. Lois from the Hiawathans and Phil from the Painters were the official attendants. Sandi's mother Doris and Harvey's former social worker, Keith, were the only guests. The reception at the Hofbrau House was bigger, however, with about twenty guests.

Sandi's mother paid for the reception which included hors d'oeuvres, buffet dinner, and a wedding cake in a private room at the Hofbrau. Doris was a teetotaler and didn't approve of holding the reception at the Hofbrau, but she went along because it was Harvey and Sandi's favorite restaurant. She wasn't planning to pay the bar tab, however. The bride and groom's finances were stretched thin by the expense of furnishing their apartment, and some of Harvey's buddies from the Painters Lodge and the Ranch were heavy drinkers, so they decided to go with a cash bar.

Harvey had hated Keith when he was his social worker, but had since come to like him. Except for Judge Anderson who stayed only for a few minutes because of a prior commitment, Keith was the only professional person at the reception. Harvey and Sandi argued about inviting Alex. Sandi said she could invite whomever she wanted because he was inviting all the Painters, so Alex was invited. But Alex heard about the argument over his invitation and decided not to attend.

Keith had seen Harvey only once since his commitment expired. He had heard that Harvey was doing okay. The phone call asking him to witness the wedding came out of the blue. He was flattered that one of his ex-clients, and a difficult one at that, would ask him to witness his wedding. And with the courthouse only a block from his office, it was a convenient excuse to leave work early on a Friday afternoon. He was a little apprehensive about the reception.

"I didn't know anyone except Harvey, so I wasn't planning to stay long," Keith remembered later.

"I noticed there were two distinct groups. The first group was rowdy, but they stood out by their appearance more than anything. Some were not dressed well enough for a wedding reception. Even most poor people have one nice outfit for special occasions, but these guys were wearing baggy, torn clothes that weren't even clean, hadn't been clean in a long time. Others of this first group had on sport coats and dress slacks, even a tie or two, but nothing matched. You know, free-store outfits.

"They were wild around the food. When the waitress brought out trays of food to replace the empty ones, they would push and shove each other and anyone else who got in the way. Once I saw the waitress balancing a tray of sausage with one hand while she tried to remove the empty tray with her other hand, and two guys started serving themselves out of the tray she was balancing. The waitress dropped the tray on the table with a thud. Two sausages bounced out and fell on the floor. A third fellow grabbed the two sausages off the floor and put them in the pocket of his sport coat.

"And they drank like it was the end of the world. The Hofbrau manager finally asked two of them to leave and two others were carried out when the party ended. During the toasting, one guy told the raunchiest joke I'd ever heard. I won't repeat it. I paid for my own beer as did others, but apparently this rowdy group was charging their beer to Harvey. I don't know how he ever paid for it. Maybe he stayed and washed dishes.

"I came to understand later that the rowdies were buddies of Harvey's from the Ranch, a drop-in center for the mentally ill. Harvey used to hang around there before he met Sandi. A lot of 'em were homeless. I suppose they ate like they hadn't eaten in a week because they really hadn't.

"The other group was much different. At first I assumed

they were friends of the bride, even though they were mostly guys. As I got introduced to them they were all from some 'lodge' or another, like the program that Harvey and Sandi were in. You would never have known from looking at these guys that they were mentally ill. I got to talking to them, and a couple were kind of goofy when you got deep into conversation, but you would never have known from looking. They were all dressed up, coats and ties. They weren't expensive clothes, suits from Sears and stuff, but they were all as clean and neat as a pin.

"And they lined up politely at the buffet table. They offered me and each other a place in line. When one of the Ranch guys butted in, the lodge guys backed away from him as if they were going to catch some disease. Some of them drank soft drinks and some drank beer, a couple quite a bit, but they paid for it as they went, and they never got sloppy or anything.

"At one point there was a series of toasts to the bride and groom, mostly from the lodge folks. It wasn't great oratory or anything, just the usual stuff people say at weddings, but it was really sweet. Several made special reference to how much Harvey and Sandi loved each other and I could see that it was true. The couple just beamed.

"The most amazing thing was how much Harvey had changed. When I worked with him he used to describe himself as a 'profligate reprobate.' I don't know what that means, but he was a guy you wouldn't have wanted to hang around with. I could see how he fit in with the Ranch crowd, and maybe was one of the worst.

"Harvey the bridegroom was completely different from the person I had known — calm, happy, considerate. He was more concerned about his guests having a good time and getting enough to eat than he was about his own needs. It was a side of Harvey I had never seen. I don't know if it was Sandi, or his meds, or the lodge program, or the fact that he was working steady, but something sure got into him; maybe all four. I guarantee you it wasn't anything I did.

"I wondered why I had been invited. Harvey read the classics and used to talk to me about symbolism. I think I was there for some symbolic function, to somehow officiate Harvey's passage from barbarism to civilized man. Or maybe I just had too much beer; I know I had a helluva good time."

Sandi's mother, Doris, paid the bar tab after all.

Harvey had applied for Social Security Disability years before coming to Tasks, but had been denied. When he got to the Hiawatha Lodge, Alex had helped him reapply and he was approved. Three years after he and Sandi were married, Harvey received a large back payment from Social Security covering the period from his original application to his ultimate approval.

Harvey and Sandi spent half of the windfall on a delayed honeymoon in Europe. They went on a packaged tour and visited eight countries in seven days. Sandi was amazed by how old everything was and how much Harvey knew about European history.

They used the other half for a down payment on a little two bedroom bungalow in Northeast Minneapolis. Sandi's mother came to live with them for a while and paid rent which helped them make the house payments. She and Harvey got along fine, but she and Sandi got on each other's nerves, and Doris didn't really like living in Minneapolis. After a year, she moved back to southern Minnesota. In the meantime, mortgage rates dropped quite a bit. So Darcy, the Lodge Social Worker, talked the woman at the bank into refinancing their house so that they could afford the payments on their income.

Harvey and Sandi both still work for Tasks Unlimited Building Services. Keith was invited to Harvey and Sandi's home to celebrate their tenth wedding anniversary. He still didn't know why. It was a wonderful meal; Sandi's a good cook.

"Here is a picture, from the Grand Forks Herald, of my son and some of his friends. He's the big man on the left."

Donna (Thomas) McPherson

CHAPTER FIVE

THE GREAT FLOOD

Lars Knutson had been a sportswriter for the *Grand Forks Herald* for 22 years. Problem was, this was a month without sports; the first such month in his career. No baseball, no track, no golf. Not even any girl sports like figure skating or volleyball. Ordinarily, Lars hated girl sports, but under the circumstances, he would have loved covering a softball game.

There wasn't even any Fighting Sioux Hockey to write about. Fighting Sioux Hockey was normally a year-round beat (the preseason, the WCHA season, the playoffs, and dry-land conditioning, *i.e.*, late spring and summer). Fighting Sioux Hockey was a big deal; there were no major league professional sports in North Dakota. None in South Dakota, eastern Montana or northern Minnesota either. The closest major league action was the Winnipeg Jets, two hundred miles and an international boundary to the north. And except for Fighting

Sioux Hockey, there weren't any big time college sports either; no division-one football or basketball, just Fighting Sioux Hockey. Fighting Sioux Hockey was practically a religion to Lars's readers.

Any other May, Lars should have been writing about dry-land conditioning, high school and Fighting Sioux baseball, preparation for the walleye opener, and dodging the dreaded girls softball assignments. But this May there was no baseball or softball, no dry-land conditioning, no dry land period. And while the walleye season technically would open on schedule, Lars couldn't imagine anybody going to the lake, because the lake had come to them.

The Red River, normally an unimpressive drainage ditch separating Grand Forks from East Grand Forks on the Minnesota side, had imitated ancient Lake Agassiz, the ice-age lake responsible for the flatness of the Red River Valley. Record snowfalls in western Minnesota and eastern Dakota had been a well-understood warning that sand-bagging would be necessary, as it is about every fourth or fifth year. But no one had any clue that an unseasonably warm March would send Grand Forks a crest twenty feet above the levee. The National Guard from both states tried to save the cities by building high dikes through Grand Forks, but they couldn't build twenty-one foot dikes all the way back upstream to Fargo. So the water just came across the beet fields. By the time the Red crested in Grand Forks, it was only three feet deep, but it was thirty miles wide.

They saved the power plant and the water treatment plant with ring dikes, and a handful of houses on the only hill in town stayed dry. Most homes and offices were built only twelve to thirty inches above the valley floor, so all basements were under water and most of the first floors had at least six inches.

The Red was back in its banks now, and the cleanup was under way. Almost every one of the 30,000 homes in the twin towns had a pile of sodden rubble in front of it. In the older section of town, where the lots were only 40 feet wide, the piles were contiguous with their neighbors on either side. Driving through this section of town, Lars felt as though he was driving down a river bed. The pavement was invisible below an inch of mud, and the unbroken pile of rubble was so high that it hid the houses behind it.

With no sports to write about, Lars was covering flood clean-up. It was the only story in town: no crime, no business, no society. There wasn't even any real weather, just sixty degrees and clear skies.

Lars's bachelor apartment was in an area which was still cordoned off to civilians. He was staying with his sister and her family in West Fargo. Every day he drove to Grand Forks, wrote a story about flood relief, and drove back to Fargo in time to drop it off at the *Herald's* temporary offices at the *Fargo Forum*. The *Herald's* presses, just a few blocks from Lars's apartment, were ruined, but they were still publishing daily out of Fargo.

Sometimes he would hang around and have a drink with the *Forum's* sportswriter, Ole Olsen. But he didn't like Olsen much. It pissed him off that Olsen was still writing sports, saved from the same river by mere topography. So mostly he filed his story and went home to watch TV with his brother-in-law.

One day, Lars was driving through the Roosevelt neighborhood. Roosevelt was composed of predominantly large, older, two-story homes. Before World War II, Roosevelt had been a fashionable upper-middle-class neighborhood. Over the last fifty years, however, Grand Forks's upper-middle-class had moved west. Even before the flood, the neighborhood was showing signs of age. Some of the homes were still occupied by families; mostly Hispanic and far from middle-class. Many of the larger homes had been converted to duplexes. Some of the aging home-owners had converted their homes into unofficial university dormitories.

Lars was bored with interviewing suburban homeowners. He was thinking of a story involving college kids, or better yet, college drop-outs with purple hair, helping their beloved landlady clean up. But he couldn't find any; he knew from the parked cars that lots of people had returned to the Roosevelt neighborhood, but he couldn't see anyone for the rubble.

Finally he came upon a pile of rubble which was only knee-high. A group of people were still hauling out wheelbarrow loads of sheet rock and piles of soggy paper. Noticing two vans with Minnesota plates, he assumed they belonged to volunteers from nearby towns outside the flood zone. Lars stopped to see if he could find a new angle, something which hadn't already been written.

They were volunteers, all the way from Minneapolis. The house they were mucking out was a group home. When the flood struck, the residents of the home, all psychos, Lars guessed, had been relocated to Jamestown State Hospital, where they had originally come from. Some of the staff had gone to Jamestown to help take care of them. The staff who stayed in Grand Forks were busy cleaning their own homes. The home was owned by a non-profit company which couldn't afford to hire a salvage crew, and they weren't eligible for the emergency loans reserved for homeowners. A group home in Minneapolis had heard about it and come up to help.

Lars was getting the story from a woman named Darcy who seemed to be in charge. While they talked, the rest of the crew continued to empty the contents of the group home onto the pile. The contents looked much like the neighboring piles, only there was more soggy paper than most.

There was one young man, thirtyish, who was heavily muscled and obviously stronger than the rest. He was carrying the heavy stuff. He looked familiar to Lars. Maybe, Lars thought, it was just because he looked athletic and Lars was accustomed to athletes.

Lars wasn't surprised to learn that the crew were volunteers who had been given time off from work. Lots of companies in Fargo had done the same. But Lars was surprised to learn the composition of the crew. Except for the woman he was speaking with, they were residents of a group home in Minneapolis. As they talked, Lars watched the crew pass back and forth. One woman looked mentally ill, but the rest he couldn't tell. He couldn't help but stare at the big guy.

Notes in hand, Lars headed for Sven's bar. He would have a beer and a burger while he wrote the story on his laptop; then he would head back to Fargo.

Settled into the back booth at Sven's, Lars was still thinking about the muscular volunteer. Suddenly it hit him. "The guy looked a lot like Dean Thomas, a legendary hockey player of Fighting Sioux fame. Could it be? Do you suppose Dean actually was nuts? That would explain a lot."

Lars thought back to the press conference twelve or thirteen years ago when Coach Grantucci announced he had signed Dean Thomas. Lars was amazed at the time. He wondered if Grantucci was bluffing. Grantucci was expected to sign all the local division one talent, but he couldn't compete in the WCHA with only North Dakota boys. Grantucci had built a WCHA dynasty and attracted international hockey attention to Grand Forks by recruiting from the hockey hotbeds of northern Minnesota and western Canada.

Dean, on the other hand, was from the Minneapolis suburbs, right in the Gophers's back yard. Grantucci got his share of the northern Minnesota talent because Grand Forks is closer to much of it than Minneapolis is, but even Grantucci had never recruited a big name player from the powerful Suburban Lake Conference.

Dean had led his high school team to the state tournament his junior and senior years. They didn't win the title either year, but Dean made a big impression on everyone who saw him play, either in person or on TV. Late in the quarter-final game his senior year, with the score tied at one, Dean destroyed Rochester's Hangsnen, a Gopher signee, with the most devastating center-ice check Lars had ever seen in a high school game. The puck popped loose and Dean's right winger skated in for an easy goal. Lars couldn't imagine how Grantucci had stolen Dean away from the Gophers.

High as the expectations were, it was no great surprise that Dean struggled during his first season with the Fighting Sioux. A lot of great high school players have trouble adjusting to college level. Grantucci wanted to make a wing out of him. Dean had played defense in high school, where he hardly ever left the ice, but he ran his team's offense from the blue line and led the team in scoring. He had the explosive speed required to play wing, and Grantucci wanted him up front. And although he was powerfully built, he was only five foot ten. Grantucci wanted taller defensemen.

Dean played some at each position his freshman year. He skated effectively here and there, but he didn't find a regular spot in Grantucci's rotation until a senior defenseman broke his leg during the last game of the WCHA season. Dean played solidly through the playoffs and convinced Grantucci he could overcome his lack of height with aggressiveness.

Dean's best season was his sophomore year. The preseason confirmed his status as a starting defenseman. By the middle of the regular season, he had established himself as one of the toughest players in the WCHA.

The moniker "Fighting Sioux" was just a team nickname, of course; North Dakota wasn't involved in any more fights than the rest of the league. But the WCHA was full of big strong kids dreaming of professional careers. Some hoped to impress the pro scouts with their speed or finesse. But every team in the conference had at least a couple of guys who knew they weren't fast enough or slick enough, and they knew the pros were looking for tough guys, sometimes known as "enforcers" or "goons." The WCHA didn't encourage toe-to-toe fist fights as the pros did, but they tolerated enough scuffling that everybody knew who the toughest guys were.

Games were scheduled in pairs on Friday and Saturday nights. Ninety percent of the fights occurred on Friday nights. The hard core goons would seek each other out during the warm-up, and all but make appointments to fight. At the first opportunity, the gloves would come off. The fights were brief because the refs would break them up, but not so quick that there weren't winners and losers. And a clear-cut winner was likely to be challenged by someone else before the game was over.

Dean wasn't a goon. He never sought out any one in particular, and he was never the first to drop his gloves. But he loved to catch an opponent with his eyes locked on the puck and drill him with a bone rattling check . If the guy didn't get up, and if one of the guy's teammates didn't believe it was a clean check and came after Dean, that was fine too. Dean didn't back down from anybody. He didn't lose any fights either. Grantucci yelled at Dean once in Denver because Denver scored the tying and winning goals on power plays while Dean was in the penalty box serving a major for roughing, but mostly he praised Dean for his competitive attitude and leadership ability.

Lars interviewed Dean almost every week that season, and wrote about him quite a bit. Lars noticed he was intense and

67

combative, but who wouldn't be if every goon in the WCHA was looking for you. He also noticed that Dean was a pretty nice kid and smarter than most hockey players Lars had known.

His attitude about the pros, for example. Although Grantucci had built a college dynasty at North Dakota, only a handful of Fighting Sioux ever made it big in the National Hockey League. And hockey players don't get million dollar signing bonuses like basketball players. Five years after finishing their college hockey careers, most of the Fighting Sioux were working for a living. And some of them weren't very good at real work; they weren't prepared for it. Almost every one of them thought they would get rich playing hockey. Not Dean. He knew that five-foot-ten defensemen were rare in the NHL.

Dean's plan was to get a teaching degree in biology or chemistry and coach high school hockey. Dean knew he would never get rich coaching, but he idolized his own high school coach and wanted to be just like him. Most of Grantucci's player's struggled to stay eligible, but Dean was pulling a B plus average in real college courses. Lars was not surprised to learn that Dean had been an honor student in high school and captain of the chess team as well as the hockey team.

The Fighting Sioux were loaded with returning talent for Dean's junior season and the fans' expectations were sky high. Lars added fuel to the fire with his September prediction that this would be the season the national championship returned to Grand Forks. Dean was one of three players Lars was hyping as all-American candidates.

Dean worked his butt off in the September skating drills; few of the Fighting Sioux could keep up with him. Lars noticed the big grin on Grantucci's face. Later, when the team began scrimmaging, the grin disappeared.

Lars had never seen anything like it. As soon as Dean stepped on the ice, he started hitting people. He would throw three, four, maybe five bone-crunching checks per sixty second shift. Grantucci and two assistant coaches told him to knock it off, but he didn't. The next time he got on the ice, boom-boom-boom. Lars had seldom seen such intensity in a big game, much less a practice. Dean would throw his body at someone, get up, skate furiously across the ice, and throw his body at someone else. He looked like he was trying to kill somebody, mostly himself. More amazing yet, he didn't seem to tire as the practice wore on. He must have hit a hundred guys by the time practice ended, but when he headed for the locker room, he looked as fresh as when he first took the ice.

Lars saw the senior co-captains corner Dean in the hallway outside the locker room. They yelled at him for quite a while. Dean appeared to listen intently and didn't have much to say. It seemed as though he understood. But at practice the next day, Dean picked right up where he'd left off. Hit somebody, get up, hit somebody. Lars began to think the getting up was more amazing than all the checking. Grantucci began to wonder if he would have six healthy players left for the first game. Several players challenged Dean to fight but each time he backed away looking bewildered. He wouldn't fight a teammate.

Halfway through the second scrimmage, Grantucci had seen enough. Dean was out of position, he wasn't working with his unit, and he was going to kill somebody. When Dean came off the ice, Grantucci barked at him to follow him to the locker room. Lars tagged along. Although Grantucci didn't usually allow sportswriters in the locker room when he was disciplining a player, this time he did not object. He thought maybe the sportswriter could help, and he needed all the help he could get.

This was the first of several conversations Grantucci had with his star defenseman that week. The second day he yelled. The third day he threatened. The fourth day he reasoned. The fifth day he pleaded. The assistant coaches tried, Lars the sportswriter tried, the trainer tried.

After practice on the fourth day of scrimmaging, Lars stood in the locker room and watched closely as Dean undressed. He was curious why Dean wasn't hurting, and what he saw amazed him even more. Dean's entire body was covered with bruises from his head to toe. He had bruises on his bruises. Yet he didn't seem to feel any pain.

Lars went into Grantucci's office and closed the door. "I think your boy's on drugs."

"I know," said Grantucci, "Gotta be those damn steroids. I should have known he didn't get that big just lifting. I've told and told these kids to go easy on that stuff but they don't listen."

"What are you going to do?"

"I'll have his test results in the morning. I'll have to kick him off the team until he gets clean."

But the test results were negative; no sign of steroids. Grantucci talked with Dean before practice. He demanded an explanation but Dean didn't have one. He promised not to touch anyone that day. But when the scrimmaging started, he was right back at it. Grantucci figured the lab results were wrong, so he dismissed him from the team.

Lars hadn't seen him since. He heard he stayed in school for a while and then one day he just disappeared. He had two years of college eligibility left, so Lars figured he would turn up playing for someone else. If he did, Lars hadn't heard about it.

Lars rushed out of Sven's bar and into his car. He hoped he could catch those Minneapolis volunteers before they left the group home so he could satisfy his curiosity. They were still there but getting ready to leave when Lars pulled up. He wanted to be certain it was him before he said anything, but they were all covered with muck. Dean's own mother would have had trouble recognizing him. So he walked up to Dean and asked him, "Do you know who I am?"

"I guess you're Lars Knutson the sportswriter, aren't you?" said Dean.

"You are Dean Thomas then!" Lars said as though it was one of the big scoops of his journalistic career, like Stanley meeting Livingstone.

Dean Thomas had been Dean Thomas all his life, so it was no big deal to him. He just said "yeah."

Lars wanted to know where Dean had been for last ten years, did he ever play hockey, and what his connection was to the group home, but the van was getting ready to leave. Dean didn't know the phone number where they were staying in Grand Forks, so he gave him his number in Minneapolis.

Dean's final week with the Fighting Sioux, in the Fall of 87, had been his first full-blown manic episode. He had never felt that good before. He felt as though he were really alive for the first time. He felt as if he had raised his game to a new level, and as soon as his teammates caught on and started playing as hard as he was, the Fighting Sioux would be unbeatable.

He heard the coaches telling him to tone it down, but he thought they meant just a little. And he intended to tone it down just a little, but when scrimmage started he felt so good that he could not stop. He had no idea why the coach dismissed him from the team. He thought it must be some kind of "mind game" intended to make him tougher. He thought they would call him back when the season started.

And then he crashed. He crashed hard. His first full-blown depression. He had felt sad before, but nothing like this. He felt so bad he thought he was going to die. He felt so bad he wanted to die. He got in his truck and headed for his mother's house to get his step-father's revolver and shoot himself.

He never got there. The truck ran out of gas halfway to Minneapolis. He started to walk. As he walked along the highway he reconsidered his plan. He didn't need a gun. He would lay down in the ditch and freeze to death. It would be less messy.

It was broad daylight, however; a highway patrolman saw him almost immediately and took him to a local hospital. Dean was transferred to a Minneapolis hospital a few days later. And a few days after that, he was released to his bewildered mother.

His records from the first hospitalization include the diagnosis "manic depression," but Dean's mother, Donna, doesn't remember hearing the term until Dean's third hospitalization. The next three and a half years were a trial for Dean and his mother. He went through numerous cycles of mania and depression. He was hospitalized seven times, usually for two to four weeks, but once for four months. Once, maybe twice, he tried suicide by taking pills. But he only made himself sick and threw up most of what he swallowed.

The first summer after dropping out of college, Dean joined the Air Force. He felt he was doing well, but at the end of basic training they sent him home with a General Discharge. They either didn't give him an explanation or he didn't understand it.

The second year he attended a local community college where he became a Certified Nursing Assistant. He got three different jobs as a Certified Nursing Assistant, but none of them lasted more than a couple of weeks. Dean liked to work and was always able to get a job. He had over a dozen during those three years. Besides nursing assistant, he worked construction, was a janitor, a skating rink attendant, but the jobs never worked out. When he wasn't in the hospital he lived with his mother.

Donna loved and was understandably proud of the easy-going hockey-star son who went off to college. The son who came home was a stranger, arguing constantly, snapping at her when she was trying to help him. She struggled and failed to understand his illness, to anticipate his moods, to help him compensate. She assumed it was her fault. "What had she done to cause this terrible disease? Had he been under too much pressure to achieve? Was it the time he had a high fever when he was a baby? Did it have anything to do with the divorce? Her subsequent remarriage?"

Once she learned the diagnosis, Donna read everything she could about manic-depression. The experts said it was hereditary, but no one in her family ever had it; and no one in her ex-husband's family that he would admit to. How could this happen? And why couldn't the doctors do anything to help him? When she took him to the hospital they put him on these terrible medications that turned him into a zombie. The treatment seemed worse then the illness. Gradually she lost faith in the medical establishment and it became more difficult to decide what to do when he got sick. She knew he needed help, but doctors and hospitals didn't seem to be the answer.

One day when Donna came home from work, Dean was backing out of the driveway. She noticed a pile of stuff in the back seat of his car. Her first thought was that he was moving out, but Dean explained he was hauling some old junk to the dump. She noticed some childhood toys and broken hockey sticks and was relieved. She had been after him to clean his room.

A few minutes after he had driven away, she walked past the door to the family rec room. After she passed the doorway it clicked in her brain that something was wrong. When she went back and looked in at the mantle over the fireplace, a wave of nausea and fear rose from her stomach. The thirty-odd trophies and medals Dean had won as a high school and Junior Olympic hockey player were gone. Donna jumped to the conclusion that another suicide attempt was in progress. Was the new Dean eliminating the old Dean as part of a twisted final gesture? She rushed to her husband's workshop and found his revolver missing. She threw up.

As soon as she could, she called the police. They had already received reports of gunshots in the area of the town dump. When they arrived at the dump, Dean was sitting in his car, shooting at the trophies he had set up on top of the dump. They took him into custody but did not pursue the potential charge of illegal discharge of a firearm. One of the officers was a hockey fan who remembered Dean. He recovered most of the trophies and medals and gave them to Dean's mother for safe keeping.

Soon afterward, Donna enrolled Dean in a residential program for people with serious and persistent mental illness. Dean liked the residence well enough, but he was bored. Donna asked the counselors at the residence to find Dean a job. They either couldn't or wouldn't. Donna heard about something called fairweather, where everybody had a job. She arranged for Dean to visit the Fairweather Training Program. To Dean, it looked the same as where he was. With his mother's encouragement, however, he transferred to Tasks.

He did not like it at first. It was a very hot summer and Tasks made everybody work regardless of the heat. Somehow he hung on and graduated to the Spirit Lodge. Four other men lived there. They worked together as janitors for four hours every evening. Some afternoons, Dean didn't feel like going to work, but Darryl, one of his lodge mates, said he had to. Once he got to the worksite, the work seemed easy.

The part he liked best was the sports. They didn't have a hockey team, but they had softball and volleyball teams with players drawn from various lodges, and they often played basketball and bowled among themselves. Dean wasn't the only athlete in the program, but he was the best hitter on the softball team. It was the first time he had really played sports since he left the Fighting Sioux. Not coincidentally, it was the first time since he got sick that he actually had fun.

After three years, his stepfather died suddenly. Dean got the idea he should move home and live with his mother. His plan was to continue playing ball for Tasks, and to continue working with the Spirits. Donna and the Spirits all agreed.

The first year went fine, but then Dean had car trouble and missed a couple of days of work. He got the car fixed, but then he missed a couple of days for no particular reason. Soon he was missing work one or two days each week. Donna was always away at her job when he was supposed to leave for work, and often he just didn't. Eventually the Spirits gave Dean an ultimatum. If he missed any more work he would be fired. Donna found out about it and got very worried. She didn't want him living with her and not working for fear he would slide back into his pre-Tasks condition. She spoke with the Tasks social worker, Darcy, and they agreed on a plan for Dean to move back to the Spirits Lodge.

Dean didn't want to go. In desperation, Donna told him he couldn't stay with her. If he wouldn't go back to the lodge she was kicking him out anyway. Dean got very angry, but in the end, he agreed to go. Dean had nothing against the Spirits Lodge; he just didn't like the idea of being in a program. He definitely resented his mother and social worker making decisions for him. Within a few days, however, he was back into the rhythm of lodge life.

Technically, Dean still has an illness called manic depression or bi-polar affective disorder. Probably always will. He takes medicine to help manage the illness and he takes another medicine to control the side effects of the first one. He lives now at the Diamond Lodge and works full time for Tasks Unlimited Building Services.

Dean is not wealthy, but he earns enough to pay for rent, groceries, his medications, gas for his car. Since he quit smoking and got a raise for taking on some extra responsibility, he is actually saving a little money. He plays hockey two nights a week in a no-checking league and he follows his old high school team, but he doesn't often think about the Fighting Sioux.

The Grand Forks flood, however, was front page news in Minneapolis. Everybody was talking about it. As the waters receded, the pictures on TV showed a horrible mess. "Maybe we should help clean that up," Dean thought, to himself at first. The next day, he shared the idea with the Diamonds and some of the Spirits and Hiawathans. Everybody thought it was a great idea except for Dale. Darcy helped Dean organize the crew, and Tasks provided the equipment. They worked hard; they got incredibly dirty. They knew their three days of work were insignificant in relationship to the terrible devastation of the flood, but they felt good about themselves on the drive back to Minneapolis.

The staff from the flooded group home in Grand Forks were impressed by the work performed by the Minneapolis group home residents, and astonished to learn that some of them worked full time and did not need Social Security. They got to talking with Darcy about it, and the following winter they visited some of the Tasks lodges. Now they have started up their own Fairweather Lodge in Grand Forks.

Donna always wanted grandchildren, and the fact that Dean has shown no inclination to get married is disappointing. Other than that, she is as proud of Dean as she ever was. She shows her friends a picture from the *Grand Forks Herald* of her son and his co-workers, all covered with muck.

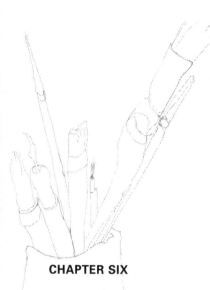

> *"People say, 'Oh that's just
> a coincidence,' but I wasn't
> born yesterday."*
>
> **Marsha Matson**
> **Hiawatha Lodge**

CHAPTER SIX

THE PLOT
AGAINST MARSHA

Nell's disappearance was the giveaway. Up until then, They had
tried to disguise their activities as random, unconnected events.
"Just a chain of coincidence," that's what They wanted her to
believe. A lot of people did, you know; bought the whole thing,
hook, line, and sinker. Mathematical chance, chaos theory, all
that crap. Marsha wouldn't have been surprised to learn that
They invented chaos theory. What a perfect cover story for all
the crap They were getting away with.

But Nell's disappearance was a new high. Or low, depending on your perspective. "She's gone. She's not here anymore.
That's all we can tell you." Like she never existed. Like it was a
perfectly natural thing for people to just vanish without a trace.
One day she's here, the next day she's not. NO EXPLANATION!

Was it a mistake? A fatal error in their otherwise elaborate
cover-up? Or did They just not care anymore? Maybe it was

just all too much effort (the lazy bastards), or maybe her credibility had been destroyed beyond the point that it mattered what she knew.

Why else would you tell an intelligent adult that Nell, her social worker, didn't exist. "She's not here. I don't know why. That information is not available. All I can tell you is that she is not here and she won't be coming back."

"So you admit that she used to work here and she used to be my social worker?"

"I didn't say that."

They obviously didn't care what she knew. It must be because They thought no one paid any attention to her anymore. And They were probably right. No one did.

Marsha could only hope that Nell hadn't been killed. Most of the people who had ever been nice to her had been. Well, maybe not Abby, that Lodge Coordinator at Tasks Unlimited. Marsha didn't know if she was dead or not. Another mysterious disappearance but at least They had bothered to invent a cover story about her getting fired for stealing Ed's valium. It wasn't believable, not if you knew Abby like Marsha did, but at least They bothered to make up a story. Marsha hoped Abby and Nell hadn't been killed.

Most of the others, Mr. Brooks, Kendell's father, Jeremy, were dead for certain. Killed by the C.I.A., F.B.I., Nixon's goons, whatever you wanted to call them. Marsha used to lie awake at night trying to figure out if They were from the C.I.A. or the F.B.I. or some other organization so secret that They don't even have initials.

But it no longer mattered to her who They were, or what They called themselves. She knew who They were. The "government," the "company," and their thousands of minions willing to sell themselves (and Marsha without her permission), into slavery. Why did the fools go along? Were they that greedy for a couple of almighty dollars? Or did they honestly believe that the exploitation of the masses by the elite was the only acceptable world order? What disaster did people think would ensue if They didn't keep the elite in power?

But why They did what They did no longer mattered either.

Whatever They called Themselves, whyever thousands of the exploited class worked so hard to keep Them in power, whoever They were, They were "Them" to Marsha. Them with a capital "T." Not that she wrote about Them or had any particular need for capitalization, but when she thought about Them at all, she thought about Them or They with a capital "T."

Nell had been her county social worker before Marsha went to the lodge; helped her get into the lodge. Abby had been her Lodge Coordinator, kind of like a social worker, while she was in the lodge. Both of them were cool; they definitely weren't Them.

She never should have left the lodge. It was her father who persuaded her after a great deal of effort. All those dinners at fancy restaurants, the gallery openings, the vacations. And always the same message: "You could have all this if you would only get your act together and finish school. I'll pay for it, whatever school you want to go to. Get out of this group home. Stop working as a janitor. You're not like these people. Stop pretending that you are mentally ill and make something of your life."

And in the end, it worked. She left.

Which raises the question of whether her father was actually one of Them, or just a stooge. Obviously he lived pretty well off the system: the country club, the trophy wife barely older than Marsha. But he didn't live that well, not well enough to be one of the people really in charge. And Marsha knew her father's love for her was sincere. Whatever his degree of compliance with Them, he would never have orchestrated the tragedy of her life.

But again it didn't really matter. Whether he was actually one of Them or just working for Them didn't matter. In the end, the fools working for Them were Them. It was the same difference.

Marsha's mother drank a lot when Marsha was growing up. And when she drank, she fought, mostly with Marsha or her father. The more she fought with Marsha's father, the more he tuned out. He buried himself in his art collecting, took up with other women, worked harder for Them, who knows. He was around some, taking Marsha to galleries, teaching her about art, but when her mother got on her case, he was no help. Marsha's only defense was to fight back. And she fought back hard.

If her mother told her to eat her broccoli, for example, she wouldn't. As an adult she likes broccoli, but even now she would never eat it around her mother. If her mother told her to do her homework, or wash the dishes, or clean her room, Marsha wouldn't do it. She knew her friends' mothers made them clean their rooms and wash the dishes once in a while, but that was different. Her friends' mothers weren't drunk.

One time, when Marsha was in the eighth grade, her mother decided she could not watch her favorite television program until she cleaned her room. Marsha ignored her and watched television anyway. Her mother turned the television off. Marsha turned it back on. Her mother turned it off. She turned it back on. Her mother turned it off. She turned it back on. Her mother slapped her. Marsha slapped her back. Her mother picked up a heavy ceramic ashtray and tired to hit her with it. She missed but Marsha kicked her so hard that she fell down and broke her wrist when she hit the floor.

Afterwards, Marsha's father took her to see a psychiatrist, Dr. Benjamin. He was okay. (Marsha sometimes wonders whatever happened to him; probably killed off with the rest.) After a couple of sessions with Marsha, Dr. Benjamin figured out that her mother was the real problem. He recommended family therapy sessions involving Marsha and both of her parents. Marsha was curious to see how that would work but she never found out; her mother refused to participate.

Marsha's conflict with her mom carried over to her schoolwork. She was pretty much the smartest kid in the whole school. At least her test scores said so. But even when her mother forgot to nag her about homework, Marsha generally refused to do any. She loved art and would spend countless hours on her art projects. She was obviously gifted, and everyone told her so. But often, if her art teacher said the least little thing she didn't like, she would refuse to turn in the project. And in her other classes, she rarely did the assignments unless something caught her fancy.

Her grades were important to her father because he wanted her to study art at a prestigious private college. She probably could have gone to the college of her father's choice anyway, but midway through her senior year of high school, she announced a surprising plan. She would attend the University of Minnesota, and become an art teacher. She felt it tragic that there were so few real artists teaching in a public system dominated by no-talent wannabes. She was going to change all that.

Her first year at the University was rather calm. She loved her art classes and tolerated the rest. She joined an organization concerned with civil rights for black people, "Negroes" they called them then. But the group was mostly middle-class white kids and they never did much except sing a few songs.

In April of her sophomore year, They, only Marsha didn't yet know it was They, assassinated The Reverend Martin Luther King. Everyone was devastated, but Marsha took it personally. She knew she had to do something besides singing.

She joined a busload of University of Minnesota students who participated in a series of demonstrations across the South. It was exciting and scary, but in retrospect, kind of uneventful compared to what some of the other northern students experienced. They got a ton of dirty looks and were even cussed at a couple of times, but nobody shot at the group Marsha was with, or ran them off the road or anything like that.

Her most memorable experience was meeting a black college student from Chicago named Kendell. He wasn't at all what she expected. The few black boys she had known tended to be loud and confident. Kendell was quiet and shy, and much better read than she was. She imagined herself falling in love with him and having his babies, but he just wanted to be friends. They exchanged letters off and on for years afterward.

She had lost interest in college by the time the bus returned to Minneapolis. A sympathetic professor had made arrangements for all the participating students to make up the exams and course work they missed, but Marsha wasn't interested. She let everything slide and ended up taking an incomplete in each of her courses, even her art courses.

She lay around her parents' house all summer. She did a little painting, but nothing much. Most of her friends had summer jobs, but she never quite got around to looking for one. Then, as her friends were winding up their jobs and heading back to school, Marsha surprised everyone by applying for and getting a job as a secretary at the Honeywell Corporation. A Fortune 500 company headquartered right there in Minneapolis,

Honeywell was into electronics, thermostats and a lot of other stuff.

To her surprise, she found she liked working better than going to school. The secretarial work was pleasant enough, and she really liked the people she worked with. She stayed there four years, despite her father's pleas to finish school. The only problem was (and Marsha didn't know it at first), Honeywell was making more than thermostats: bombs and mines, for example. (Anti-personnel bombs and mines to be specific. Weapons which were being used to kill people in Vietnam.) Marsha wasn't making bombs: she was a secretary in the SSHS Division, which was working on the design for a new thermostat. Nor was anyone she knew personally making bombs. But someone at Honeywell, someone working for the same corporation she was, was making horrible weapons.

When she first started working there, she signed some papers and was given a security clearance. She didn't think anything of it at the time. Later, a man from the Defense Department came around and spoke to all the employees of Marsha's division. He said that Honeywell was involved in several top secret projects critical to national defense. They had to be careful, the man said, not to reveal these secrets to anyone. "What nonsense," Marsha thought at first. "No one in SSHS knows any secrets related to national security." Even so, the man kept coming around every couple of months to lecture them on keeping secrets.

The lectures didn't bother her, but her growing realization of Honeywell's involvement in the Vietnam War did. She had maintained contact with some of her friends from the civil rights group, and also with the guy from Chicago, to whom she wrote often. All were increasingly critical of U.S. involvement in the war, and of weapons production by greedy private companies.

She spoke of her concerns to her boss, Mr. Brooks, a very nice man whom she respected. He was as critical of the war effort as any of her friends, and disappointed that Honeywell was involved. But he assured her that nothing he did, and therefore nothing she did, had any military function. He was a man of strong principle. He said he would quit before he would help design weapons, especially for an immoral war.

Marsha was torn between her confidence in Mr. Brooks and her horror at what she was reading in the anti-war litera-ture. When she talked with Mr. Brooks she felt assured. The bomb makers were an entirely separate division, almost like a separate company. It had nothing to do with them. But then her friends would show her an article detailing Honeywell's role in the killing and maiming of innocent people and she'd feel terrible. She stopped telling people where she worked. She anguished before coming to work each day.

And then They killed Mr. Brooks. They said it was an early morning heart attack, but it didn't make sense. The man was thirty-nine years old, excellent health, thin as a rail, didn't drink. And one morning he rolls over at five a.m. and dies. "Come on!"

No one working in Mr. Brooks's SSHS Division believed it was that simple. There had to be more to the story. But people were cautious about sharing their individual theories, and Marsha wasn't yet aware of how extensive Their control was. Later, Marsha understood it clearly. They killed him somehow, and made it look like a heart attack. Marsha wasn't certain if They killed him because he knew too much, or because he refused to work on weapons production. Exactly why was another one of those things which didn't really matter.

But even at the time, not fully understanding what was going on, Marsha was terrified. It was obvious there was some connection between those absurd lectures about their work on thermostats being top secret, and the untimely death of the head of the division.

Her first thought was to quit. But would they let her? Maybe Mr. Brooks was trying to quit and that's what got him killed. Of course he knew more; she didn't really know anything which seemed all that important. But maybe she knew things she didn't know she knew. Or maybe somebody thought she knew more than she really did.

It was just too risky to quit without a cover story.

Fortunately, her father was still imploring her to return to college and art. She started talking to her co-workers about all the pressure she was getting from her father. "He is incessant," she told them. He could not be appeased by anything short of her quitting her job, which she loved. Simultaneously, she was as little help to Mr. Graham, Brooks's replacement, as possible. She was polite and cooperative, but suddenly she didn't know how to do anything, or where to find anything. After four or five weeks, Mr. Graham suggested she follow her father's advice. She escaped with her life!

While working at Honeywell, she had rented the upstairs half of a very nice duplex near the lakes. When she enrolled in the Minneapolis College of Art, she took a smaller apartment in a less fashionable area near the college. Her father had offered to help with the rent on the duplex, but she wanted to get closer to school to immerse herself in the arts.

Hers was one of sixteen modest units in a two-and-a-half-story walkup. It was two blocks from MCA, on the edge of a "transitional" neighborhood. "Transitional" was Minneapolis-speak for an area into which black people were moving. The art students, with their typically liberal orientation, were above all that. At least at first. When Marsha first moved in, there was a lot of talk about how wonderful it was to live in an integrated neighborhood. People bragged about having black friends.

Marsha told a couple of people about her black "boyfriend" in Chicago.

But then the break-ins started. One by one, apartments were broken into and cleaned out of saleable items. Sometimes the victim would replace the TV, the stereo, buy some new clothes, only to be broken into again. And this time the thieves got all new stuff, instead of old junk.

At first the victims would call the police, but it didn't take long to figure out that the police were useless. They never caught the burglars and no one ever got their stuff back. The tenants held building meetings to discuss security strategies. They met with the landlord to demand better locks. Nothing worked. The break-ins continued.

Marsha's apartment was broken into once. Some stuff was taken, nothing especially valuable. None of her original art. She replaced what she needed with money she had saved up working at Honeywell. She did not get hit a second time. It was no big deal to her. Others were less fortunate, burglarized multiple times, unable to afford replacing everything. Ultimately, unable to afford insurance, they were outraged.

The police never caught the burglars in the act or in possession of stolen items; they never collected enough evidence to arrest or charge any particular person. But they intimated that they knew one thing about the people responsible — their race. "You've got to expect this in a transitional neighborhood," they said.

Despite their counter-cultural dress and lifestyles, the MCA students were predominately white, mostly from middle-class backgrounds. Except for Marsha, they were quick to take the hint. They were angry at being ripped off, and they needed someone to blame. Marsha couldn't believe how quickly their attitudes changed. Within a matter of months, the noble and downtrodden black folk, whose liberation movement the students had enthusiastically endorsed, whose beauty and dignity was an inspiration for much of the students' art, became "thieving Niggers" whose only purpose in life was to rip Whitey off. Marsha couldn't handle it. Her art suffered and she stopped attending class. She slipped into an unremitting depression. At her father's suggestion, she abandoned her apartment and moved in with her parents.

It was a horrible mistake. If she hadn't been so depressed, she would have known that it would be.

Nothing had really changed. Her mother was still drinking, still nagging; her father was never around. The only thing different was that Marsha now knew what she had not known growing up: that everyone, including herself, was crazy.

She was twenty-four years old and living with her parents. Nixon was bombing Cambodia and the University students, the only group of people she felt any affinity for, were on strike over it. She wanted to go on a strike of her own, but what could she be on strike from? She had already dropped out of school for the second time, and she had no job.

At the height of her depression, the second piece of the puzzle explaining how the world really worked arrived in the mail. Kendell wrote to say that his father had died in a mysterious fire. His parents' home, on a quiet street in a quiet black neighborhood on the south side of Chicago, had mysteriously burst into flames in the middle of the night. The Fire Marshall could not determine how the fire started. Kendell's mother and teenage sister escaped, just barely. According to the coroner, a contributing factor to the father's death was that he was drunk. "Highly unlikely," Kendell wrote, "because Father was a very moderate drinker. He usually had one beer in the evening after supper. Never more! I've never seen him drunk in my life."

A second mysterious and untimely death. Something very odd was going on. Later, when Marsha understood things

89

better, it was obvious. For whatever reason, They killed Kendell's father. Just like They killed Mr. Brooks.

The news from Kendell, even though she did not completely understand what was going on, exacerbated Marsha's depression. It was all she could do to drag herself out of bed by midafternoon. Her mother, always drunk by mid-afternoon, nagged her incessantly. One afternoon, she just couldn't take any more of it. She grabbed an empty wine bottle off the kitchen counter and conked her mother over the head with it. Her mother dropped to the floor unconscious. After trying unsuccessfully to revive her, Marsha called the police and told them what happened. By the time the ambulance arrived, her mother had regained consciousness, but they took her to the hospital anyway. Except for a nasty lump on the head, she was fine.

Her parents declined to file charges. They recognized Marsha's need for psychiatric treatment. Her father arranged for her admission to a very expensive residential program in a nearby state.

One of the specialties of the clinic was Silence Therapy. Most afternoons, Marsha was placed in an absolutely soundproof room for about four hours. There was no sound except for what she made herself, and she was encouraged not to make any. The room was cool and very brightly lit to discourage sleeping. The idea was to sit there, in absolute silence, and get your head straight.

At first, Marsha thought it was weird, but after a while she rather enjoyed it. She didn't know if her head was getting straight or not, but with help from a Silence Therapy Coach, she learned how to concentrate and figure things out. It was during Silence Therapy that she began to understand the connection between the war in Vietnam, blaming everything on black people, and the deaths of Mr. Brooks and Kendell's father.

She also met a boy named Jeremy while at the clinic. He

was from a small town in Southern Minnesota, and diagnosed schizo-affective, same as she. Like her, he was also artistic, though more of a poet and musician than a painter. She shared her developing theory about who killed Mr. Brooks and Kendell's father, and Jeremy agreed that the F.B.I. was probably involved.

She stayed at the clinic until her father's money began to run out. He had not succeeded in getting his insurance to pay for it, and it was costing him $7500 a month. The clinic advised him Marsha should stay longer, but after sixteen months and $120,000, he decided she had received enough treatment.

She actually did feel better as she left the clinic than she had on arrival. She found an apartment in Minneapolis and a job at a "gallery." (It was really a store selling reproductions of over-rated art to people with not enough money for the real thing and even less taste, but she didn't mind.)

The real problem was with her apartment. She took the apartment in September, before the heating season had begun. By November, it was obvious that something was wrong with the heating system; it worked only intermittently. By December, and it was a cold December that year, the furnace was going out, for a day or two at a time, at least once a week.

All the tenants were complaining to the caretaker and the landlord when they could find either one of them. Finally, a sizeable group of tenants cornered the caretaker, the landlord, and a repairman hired to fix the furnace. The trio offered up a most peculiar explanation: someone, who knew whom or why, kept stealing critical parts, rendering the furnace inoperable. Most of the tenants rejected the explanation as unbelievable. But Marsha, who had not been at the meeting, heard the story second hand, and believed. And she knew who. The same people who killed Mr. Brooks and Kendell's father.

Whatever the plot was, it was the last thing Marsha needed, her mental health not being so great to start with. She ended up in the psych ward of a local hospital. The hospital referred her to the county for services, and the county assigned Nell (who would later disappear without a trace) as her social worker.

Nell was great. She was the first person Marsha had met since she became ill, who both understood her illness and cared about her as a person. Her father cared about her, so did Kendell for that matter, but they didn't understand her schizo-affective disorder. The doctors, on the other hand, seemed to understand the illness, but they didn't really care about her as a person. Jeremy shared her diagnosis, and he kind of cared about her, but he was wrapped up in trying to cope with his own illness. Only Nell really understood and really cared.

When a return to the apartment without heat (parts were still being stolen) resulted in a second hospitalization, Nell suggested the Lodge Program. The Hiawatha Lodge was a small group home. Besides Marsha, there were three men and two other women who lived there. There was a staff person named Abby who checked in with the group several times each week, but she did not live there. The people who lived there all had mental illness, like Marsha. Not exactly like Marsha, since they all had different forms of mental illness, or at least different symptoms. But the common thread was that they all had experienced difficulty living by themselves. And, like Nell, they understood mental illness, but they also cared about Marsha. They didn't care about her right away, of course; that took time. But they cared about each other; she could feel that the day she moved in.

Two of the guys, Ed and Dale, argued with each other all the time. It got kind of old to listen to them arguing all day, but there was a weird kind of attachment involved. And although everybody at Hiawatha Lodge had problems; they had strength also.

Ed did all the driving. His brother, Everett, who knew everything there was to know about janitorial work, was the Crew Chief at the County Courthouse where they cleaned. Jan kept the kitchen spotless; Lois was a fantastic cook.

Marsha, who had done some basic bookkeeping when she worked at Honeywell, became the Lodge Treasurer. Each of the Hiawathans paid a monthly membership fee to Hiawatha Lodge. Out of these funds, Marsha had to pay for the utilities, gas for the van, all the groceries, the house and vehicle leases to Tasks, and so forth.

Before she moved in, Dale had been the treasurer, but he wasn't very good at it. Abby, the staff person, kept needing to re-calculate everything and they were never really certain how much money they had left. Abby was glad to have Marsha take over because it made her job easier, the lodge members felt better about having one of their own keep the books, and under Marsha's control their cash reserves grew steadily.

The whole setup was pretty nice, the best place Marsha had ever lived.

The only problem was the janitorial work. It wasn't the work itself so much as her father's attitude about janitorial work. Everyone at the Hiawatha Lodge worked together as janitors at the courthouse. It wasn't a great job but it wasn't that bad. Marsha didn't mind it. In fact, she really liked working with the other Hiawathans. Driving to work and back in the Hiawatha Van, sharing supper with the Hiawathans halfway through the shift, going out for pizza together after work on Fridays — the normality of it all was comforting.

Her father hated it. "A brilliant and talented girl like her? It didn't make any sense. Working as a janitor and living at the Hiawatha Lodge was fine for some of these people; for some of them it was the best they could do. But Marsha was a gifted artist from a good family." (He was divorcing his wife because she wouldn't stop drinking, but that was beside the point.) They weren't the kind of people who did janitorial work.

Marsha's attachment to the lodge was strengthened when she learned of Jeremy's suicide. His drowned body turned up in the Mississippi River. The official story was that he had been seen, two days earlier, jumping from the bridge connecting LaCrescent, Minnesota with LaCrosse, Wisconsin. It was a convenient story, given Jeremy's diagnosis and where his body turned up. But the motorist who reported the jump had only seen someone climbing on the railing, not actually jumping, and she never saw the climber's face. Another interesting fact, which Marsha was able to discover, was that the coroner reported bruising, but no broken bones. If Jeremy, a former high school swimmer, hadn't broken anything on impact from the jump, then how did he drown in the warm and slow-moving river?

Jeremy's family was not responsive to Marsha's suggestions of foul play; they wanted to put it behind them and get on with their lives. But Marsha knew. Jeremy was Their third victim. Third that she knew of; there were probably thousands. No one else understood this. No one else saw the connection. Abby, the Hiawatha Coordinator, was at least supportive on a personal level. Always willing to listen, never dismissing her theory as paranoid. Her father, on the other hand, wouldn't allow her to talk of such things.

Her father said she was getting crazier, the longer she lived with other crazy people. He wanted her to quit her janitorial job, leave the lodge, and finish college. His primary tactic was to take her shopping, to fancy restaurants, to exclusive gallery openings, even expensive holidays to London and Paris. His message was consistent, "This is the world you belong in. And if you would only finish college, and maybe graduate school, you could live like this full time. And you could pay your own way or meet some boy from a similar background. You don't belong doing janitorial work, and you're not really crazy, you just think you are."

It was a persuasive message. As much as she enjoyed Lois's Chicken Paprika, it didn't really match up with a gourmet meal on the banks of the Seine. Eventually she capitulated. She took an apartment and enrolled in the Fine Arts program at the University.

It wasn't long before They started up again. Some of the funny stuff going on might have been coincidental, but there was too much funny stuff for it all to be coincidental. Someone was behind it, and Marsha knew it was Them.

The repeated break-ins, for example. Someone kept breaking into her apartment but never taking much — once her watch, another time her favorite pair of jeans, several grocery items she had purchased the day before, the rent check she had gotten from her father and laid on the kitchen table to give to the landlord, sometimes nothing at all. Often, someone would come in while she was out, rummage around through her things, and not take anything; or maybe They took something she never even missed. She often wondered what They were looking for. Was it possible They photographed her things? Why would They do that? What did They want?

It didn't matter.

She called the intrusions "break-ins," but most of the time They seemed to have a key. She would demand that the landlord change her lock and give her the only key; not even the landlord or the caretaker was allowed to have one. Nevertheless, within a few days, a week at the most, They would be coming in and out of her apartment at will. In between, They would try to break in. More than once she showed the caretaker fresh marks on the door jamb where They had tried to pry the new lock

95

open, but he didn't care. He was probably in on it.

She knew They had been there, even when They didn't take anything, by virtue of various strategies she devised. Often she would run a piece of scotch tape from the door to the door jamb. Twice she left her fourth floor apartment, after taping extensively, by propping open the stairway window, and crawling to it from the window of her apartment around the corner. The first time wasn't so bad, but the second time she lost her balance for a second and almost fell. She was afraid to do it after that.

Sometimes her tape was undisturbed. More frequently it was broken or pulled loose. Sometimes They tried to replace or reattach the tape, sometimes They didn't. She couldn't tell if They didn't notice she had taped or They just didn't care.

It didn't really matter.

After They stole her second pair of jeans, she gave up wearing jeans. She wore her pajama pants all the time. Even if she went out, to the store or wherever, she wore her pajama bottoms instead of pants. After a while she started wearing the tops as well, instead of a bra and a shirt. Pretty soon she gave up changing clothes all together. She would buy a pair of pajamas, rush home and put them on, and wear them day and night until they fell apart. Then she would put a robe or a jacket on and buy a new pair.

One day when she was out and about in her pajamas, she ran into Ed and Everett from Hiawatha Lodge. She was glad to see them, but they didn't seem happy to see her. They spoke to her in a very odd manner, as though they thought there was something wrong with her. In the course of the conversation, she asked about Abby.

"She got fired," Everett said.

"Fired? What do you mean? Fired by whom?" she asked, thinking only the Hiawatha Lodge members could fire her. And why would they ever do that?

"Fired by Tasks Unlimited," said Everett.

"She was pinching my valium," Ed said.

She asked them a hundred questions about this but they
didn't seem to want to talk about it. Marsha couldn't tell if they
were covering something up or if they just didn't know much.

"She's not dead, is she?"

They looked very strange and didn't answer. She asked
them three more times.

"No," they finally answered with a funny look on their
faces.

Marsha was scared. As scared as she had been when she
was working for Honeywell and They killed Mr. Brooks. Nell
was the only person she could think of to turn to. She went to
the county services office where Nell worked. Not any more!

"Where is she?" Marsha demanded.

"She is not here," They said.

"You said that already, but where is she?"

"Look, Ms. Matson, you said your name was Marsha
Matson, right? According to the computer, you no longer have
an active case with Hennepin County Mental Health. If you
need a social worker, you'll have to go through intake as if you
were a new case. Assuming you are still a Hennepin County
resident, we can get you a new social worker within a couple
of days."

"Why won't you tell me what happened to her?"

"Nothing happened to her, she just doesn't work here any
more."

"So where does she work now?"

"We don't know, and if we did we couldn't tell you."

"Why not?"

"We have been around and around on this, Ms. Matson.
We can't tell you any more than we already told you."

"Which is what? That she's not here? That she used to work here and nothing happened to her. But now she doesn't work anywhere? Oh, wait a minute. You're not even admitting she used to work here, are you? A lot of people saw her, you know, she had other clients besides me."

"You'll have to go through intake if you need a worker."

So it had come to this. Mr. Brooks and Kendell's father and Jeremy were killed, Nell and Abby had disappeared. And now they weren't even bothering to make up a cover story.

Things continued to spiral downwards for a while. Old friends from the Hiawatha and other lodges would see her on the street once in a while, wearing old rags which had formerly been pajamas. Her father lost touch with her when she lost her apartment. He filed a missing person report with the police, but nothing came of it. She slept on the streets, sometimes in shelters. She didn't really want anyone to find her.

Eventually the police did find her and took her to the county psych ward. After she stabilized back on her medication, they sent her to a halfway house. Nobody at the halfway house worked; they just hung around waiting to get sick again. Marsha didn't want to get sick again. She called Tasks Unlimited. She found out that Hiawatha was willing to give her another chance, so she moved back into the lodge.

But They weren't entirely out of her life.

She got excited about Jimmy Carter during his Presidency. When he ran the first time, Marsha's life had been too much of a mess for her to pay much attention. But now that her life was coming together, she became aware of how much she liked Carter. He was running for re-election against this fool Reagan and his voodoo economics. Marsha decided to get involved.

She went down to the local Carter campaign office and

signed on as a volunteer. She was willing to do anything except that she wasn't available early evenings on week nights because that was when the Hiawathans worked. Mostly the Carter people assigned her to pass out literature. But They showed up, and wouldn't let Marsha do her job. Every time she tried, They hassled her. Sometimes it was store clerks, or ticket takers, or people raking their leaves. "Hey you," They would yell, "get away from here. You can't pass out this crap around here."

Often Reagan goons would show up, people who had no more right to express Their opinion in a public place than she did, but acted as though They owned the shopping mall or the street corner. Men much bigger than she would rip the literature out of her hands, yell at her about Carter being stupid, and prevent her from distributing the literature to others.

When she explained what was happening to her, the Carter people suggested she seek out a policeman if it happened again. But the police were on Their side! Sometimes the police would hassle her directly without anyone else involved. Sometimes the police threatened to arrest her.

She thought the Carter people would support her. Surely they weren't with Them, it wouldn't make sense. But oddly enough, the Carter people weren't supportive. (None of her campaign co-workers were experiencing these problems. They sent someone with her a couple of times, during which They didn't show up.) The Carter people gave her counter-productive advice, and when They continued to hassle her, the Carter people stopped giving her assignments. "We'll call you when we need you," they said, but they never called.

It served them right that Reagan won the election.

Mostly they leave Marsha alone now. She still lives at the Hiawatha Lodge and still goes to work every evening. The Hiawathans have really gotten wild on Friday nights; sometimes they go out for Vietnamese food instead of pizza. She loves the Hiawathans except when they nag her about getting her lodge chores done.

She rarely sees her father anymore. He has a new wife and a new life, which Marsha just doesn't fit into.

Her mother lives alone. Marsha goes to visit her once a month. She always asks Marsha for money and Marsha always gives it to her. Marsha knows she is only going to buy liquor with it, but it doesn't matter.

"Man, I told you he was dead! How's he gonna take me anywhere?"

Silas Washington
Spirit and Diamond Lodges

CHAPTER SEVEN

THE CHEESEBURGER KID

Silas was proud to be a psychiatric patient. It was his second career, and he considered it to be a big improvement over his first. The psychiatric hospital and the halfway house were superior to the accommodations to which he was accustomed. Less boring, a whole lot safer, and he was meeting a better class of people.

He felt he was better at it.

The lodge training program at Tasks Unlimited was based on "steps." If you accomplished certain things, you got promoted to the next step, where there were more privileges, fewer restrictions, higher expectations, and increased responsibilities. And when you mastered the expectations of that step, there was yet another. He was vaguely aware of similar structures in other institutions he had been in, school, for example. But he didn't learn fractions in the fifth grade and they still sent him to the sixth grade where he didn't learn them either. At Tasks, Silas was actually learning things and then getting rewarded specifically for what he had done.

He had never succeeded at anything before.

In school, he had been a polite and friendly kid, well-liked by his teachers, but strictly a "D" student. He liked sports, but he was certainly no star athlete, even if he had stayed in school.

Nor had he experienced success in his first career, which was crime. He was a mugger for ten years, but he never made any real money at it. And he got caught a lot.

At least for Silas, crime did not pay.

He was strictly a purse and wallet man. Just strip the cash and dump the rest. A couple of times he tried to use the credit cards he came up with, but it never worked. Not even the dumbest clerk would believe it was really his card. One time, he sold some cards to a guy who bought cards, but he only got $5 for three cards (later he heard the going rate was $10 per card), and he never even got the $5. The guy said he would pay him later, but he never did. When he tried to talk to him about it, the guy said the cards were worthless and Silas should pay him for his trouble.

He didn't mess with jewelry either. Jewelry didn't interest him much personally as he didn't have a girlfriend, and his mom and sister didn't approve of stealing. He knew a guy who bought stolen jewelry, but the guy was only interested in high quality merchandise. Silas tried to sell him some jewelry a couple of times, but the guy said it was "costume."

So he worked strictly for cash. Unattended purses were his favorite thing. But unattended purses were rare, especially when he needed money the most. His second favorite thing was a purse dangling so loosely he could sneak up and snatch it from the owner without resistance. But he was never good at sneaking up. Women would usually see him coming and tighten their grip on the purse. His primary method of operation, therefore, was to confront people and demand their money.

He learned, partly by trial and error and partly by watching others, that the more angry and menacing he could appear, the better his chances. He made an effort, therefore, to appear as angry and menacing as possible. His main asset was his black skin. White Minnesotans (and most are white) were quite willing to give any black man the benefit of the doubt on the question of menace. He enjoyed the additional advantages of being young, heavy set, and very ragged in his dress and hygiene.

His personality, however, worked against him. His nature was polite and friendly. Polite and friendly might have been assets to other criminal specialties like swindling or embezzlement, but they were liabilities to a street tough. He knew other street toughs who could separate a tourist from his money with an icy stare and a gruff tone of voice, intimidation so subtle that it was difficult to prosecute: "I asked him for the time and he gave me $40. Is that a crime?"

But try as he might, Silas could not master the icy stare or the gruff tone. His best efforts to growl, "gimme your wallet," came across as a polite request. Sometimes it worked, more often not.

A few people turned and ran or screamed for help. Respectable black people tended to admonish him, "get away from me, you filthy hoodlum," or "you should be ashamed of yourself." Respectable white people generally ignored him. They averted their eyes and kept on walking. They might quicken their pace and detour slightly, but otherwise they acted as though they could neither see nor hear him. Sometimes he felt as if he didn't even exist.

Try as he might, he could not consistently intimidate people with his voice or appearance. Consequently, he found it necessary to employ a weapon of some sort for added threat.

Guns were out of the question. The noise and the mess they made attracted a lot of attention. (Technically that was a problem only if you pulled the trigger, but he was afraid of them going off by accident.) He never used one.

Knives were much better, not as noisy, messy, dangerous or expensive. He liked knives and used them on occasion. (Just for show, of course; he never stabbed anyone.) He found that the best kind of knives were those with blades which folded or retracted. A butcher knife was plenty scary, but walking around with a butcher knife attracted attention. A guy walking around with a big knife was as likely to be arrested before he robbed anyone as after.

Silas' problem with pocket knives was that he had enormous trouble keeping track of them. He'd get a nice knife, have it for a couple of days, a week at most, and then he'd lose it. Several times, he reached into his pockets as he approached likely victims, only to find his pockets empty. It was unnerving to find oneself unarmed in the middle of an attempted armed robbery. So when he had a pocket knife, he would frequently take it out to make sure he still had it, which attracted almost as much attention as walking around with a butcher knife.

In the beginning of his career, he tried to keep a knife with him at all times, but more than half the time, he was without one. He was constantly trying to buy or steal one to replace one he had lost. Eventually it was just too much trouble. He never seemed to have one when he needed it most.

It was trouble enough keeping track of his one most valued possession: his walkman radio with headphones. He played the radio and wore the headphones all the time. Even when mugging people. Even though it hurt his credibility as a menace and occasionally impaired his get-away, he always wore the phones. Second to feeding himself, and maybe not that, he worried about batteries, connections, and keeping a radio going.

He actually went through several walkmans. (They weren't always made by Walkman, of course; he called any radio with headphones a walkman, regardless of the brand.) Some had the radio mounted right on the phones, which got heavy when he wore them all day; and some which clipped onto his shirt or into his pocket connected by a troublesome wire to the phones. It was a hassle either way.

Mostly he bought his walkmans retail. He shoplifted batteries on occasion, but the one time he tried to shoplift a walkman he got caught. (Sneaky was not his best suit.) Occasionally he bought a walkman from a professional shoplifter, or maybe a crackhead who needed the money. But Silas tended to develop emotional attachments to his walkmans, and was never in the market for a second walkman to lug around, until the first one was lost or broken. And you can't always find a crackhead when you need one, so retail was usually the most efficient option.

Making certain he maintained possession of a working walkman was a major source of stress in his life. Keeping track of a pocketknife was exponentially more stressful. Without reading self-help books, he instinctively recognized the need to simplify.

So for most of his career, his weapons of choice were more basic. He found he was much more successful at conveying menace with a club in his hand than just making a fist. A club might be improvised from a chunk of concrete, a two-by-four, a pipe. "Debris" you might call it if you were looking for a general category. (Not that Silas was concerned about what to call it.)

Debris was really basic and easy to find. Pick some up, threaten somebody with it, take their purse or wallet, and throw the debris away. Theoretically, the victim could have picked up the discarded weapon and threatened Silas with it, but that never seemed to happen. And since debris was widely available,

Silas did not need to carry it around between uses or worry
about losing it. When it came time to mug someone, he would
look around for any heavy object to use as a weapon. Anything
from a rock the size of a softball to a bent and tangled connection of angle-iron would work, anything he could lift and use to
threaten someone.

Silas' motivation for mugging was as basic as his choice of
weaponry. He was hungry, or thirsty, or needed a new walkman.
He never mugged people for the fun of it. Robbery was work,
not recreation.

Sometimes, if the proceeds of a mugging were sufficient,
he might purchase some luxury such as clothing or shoes, weed
or crack, a cab ride or a movie ticket, a room for the night or
even a woman. He could spend $200 real quick if he happened
to acquire that kind of money. But he would never have
mugged anyone just to get high or get laid, only to eat or to
get a walkman.

He loved to eat. When his resources allowed, he would eat
four, five, even six times a day. His tastes in food ran as basic as
his taste in weaponry: steak, potatoes, apple pie, and especially
cheeseburgers. But when hungry, he would eat anything he
could get, even vegetables. He was not averse to eating out of
garbage cans when times were hard, and they often were. It
would be a mistake to overestimate Silas' success as a mugger.
He succeeded often enough to avoid losing weight, but just
barely.

Without a weapon, people generally ignored him. With a
weapon, people seemed genuinely afraid of him, but they were
more likely to run away than to hand over their money.
Sometimes he tried to chase them, but he was embarrassingly
slow-footed for a young man. Old people and women in high

heels often outran him. His best potential victims were old rich people too frightened to run, but they were scarce downtown after dark.

He suspected that somewhere, in the suburbs, or the afflu-ent neighborhoods of the city, rich people were walking around in the dark with wallets and purses full of cash. But he wasn't clear where these places were or how to get there. And how would he get back downtown? He couldn't very well tell a cabbie, "Take me out to the suburbs where there are rich people, then wait around while I rob one, then I'll pay you on the way back." (He never actually tried this, but he didn't think cabbies were likely to go for it.)

So Silas stayed downtown where people were streetwise. It was hard to make a living mugging people who were streetwise. They were afraid of a young man who was threatening to hit them with a club, but fear alone was often not enough to close the deal. Even when he was wielding a good-sized piece of debris, some people ignored him.

Sometimes he had to club them. Most people were more willing to give up their wallets after he had clubbed them in the head a couple times.

Silas did not enjoy hurting people. But he took no care not to hurt them. He just wanted money. Later, when he was in Spirit Lodge, Darcy asked him if he had ever hurt anyone when he mugged them.

"No," he answered quickly.

"How is it that you clubbed people in the head but it did not hurt them?"

"Well, hurt a little, you know, but not bad. Not serious."

"You say you mugged hundreds of people but you never hurt anyone seriously?"

"No."

"Are you certain?"

"I don't know. I guess not."

"Doesn't it bother you that you might have killed someone or crippled them for life?"

"I never killed anyone."

"How do you know."

"They never said I did. The cops would've said."

"But how does it make you feel to know that you could have killed someone, and may have hurt someone bad?"

"I don't think about it." Silas then thought quietly for a long time. "I won't do it again," he finally added.

When he thought back on it, he kind of wished he had chosen a different first career. Maybe he could have flipped burgers or worked in a gas station. At the time, he never thought about a job. He had never imagined that anyone would have hired him. He didn't have any marketable skills that he knew of; he wasn't even good at mugging people. The fact that his criminal career lasted ten years had nothing to do with his success rate or his skill at avoiding arrest. He was arrested more than forty times.

Silas really liked hamburgers, especially McDonald's. His very favorite restaurant was the McDonald's in the heart of downtown Minneapolis. When he had money, he might eat there four or five times a day. When he did not have money, he could often be found in McDonald's thinking about getting money. Usually this meant walking from McDonald's to the nearest construction site to find a weapon, wandering from there to find a victim, and then back to McDonald's to eat. The availability of construction varied with the season and the availability of victims varied with the time of day. Worst case scenario, the round trip could take up to three hours. Best case, only three minutes.

In the summer, there would often be street repair or a major building project within a block of McDonald's; on occasion, right in front of it. Several times, Silas found it possible to mug people on the sidewalk directly in front of McDonald's.

On each of these occasions, Silas was still enjoying his Big Mac, or maybe the last of his fries, when the police arrived to arrest him. He never mastered the principle of putting distance between himself and the crime scene. It wasn't that he returned to the scene of the crime, like a flawed mastermind in a mystery story; he barely left.

Often, the victim or a witness would observe Silas fleeing into McDonald's, and he was not likely to have emerged when the police arrived to investigate. The victim or witness would point excitedly toward McDonald's as they tried to describe Silas to the police. But the police didn't need a description; they recognized the pattern. It got to the point that if there was a mugging in downtown Minneapolis, the first thing the police did was to check McDonald's to see if Silas was there. If he was, they would arrest him on principle, whether he matched the description or not.

Minor street crime such as purse-snatching or even mugging was not a high priority for the local criminal justice system. They would charge him with the crime, assign him a public defender, arraign him in court where he pled not guilty, schedule a trial date, and release him. Barring weekends or holidays, he would be back on the streets within forty-eight hours, often less. They would feed him in jail, but he would get hungry again within a few hours of being released, and reoffend. One week he mugged a guy, was arrested and charged, was released, snatched a purse, was arrested and charged, was released, mugged a woman and was arrested; and it was only Thursday.

Even though he wasn't always caught, he would usually have four to a dozen charges pending by the time his first trial date came up. The prosecutor knew that the judges were reluctant to waste taxpayer's money on even one jury trail for street scum like Silas, much less a dozen. And who knew if the witnesses would show up. So in the end Silas would plead guilty to one of the crimes and the other charges, regardless of how many, would be dropped.

His first guilty plea rolled six potentially adult charges into one juvenile charge. He was sent to a juvenile corrections facility until his eighteenth birthday, four months away. His first adult sentence was even shorter, sixty days in the workhouse for eight arrests rolled into one purse-snatching, followed, soon after his release, by four more arrests and a sentence of six months in the workhouse.

Twelve arrests during the seven months following his release from the workhouse bought Silas a ticket to prison, in this case, the minimum security facility for young men at Duck Lake. He was sentenced to twenty-four months and served fourteen. There were optional vocational training programs available at Duck Lake to teach young men a trade, but as Silas already had a trade, he took no interest.

His trade led to five more arrests and another guilty plea. This time he was sentenced to eight years in St. Cloud. Always the model prisoner, he served twenty-eight months, plus three months at a half-way house.

He lived with his sister for a couple of months after the half-way house. He was supposed to have a job, but it didn't work out. His sister gave him hamburger money to keep him out of trouble and he intended to stay clean somehow. That didn't work out either.

The cops noticed him at his favorite restaurant eating a Big Mac purchased with his sister's money. They didn't believe his story but they didn't have any unsolved muggings at the moment. Two hours later, someone was mugged by a black guy about six blocks away. Silas was still at McDonald's working on some fries (he hadn't left), so they arrested and charged him.

He did not find the experience of being arrested and charged with a crime he had not committed to be much different from being arrested for a crime he had committed. Same racist cops, same smelly jail cell, same indifferent lawyers and judges. He made one attempt to explain to his lawyer that he had been at McDonald's the entire time, but the lawyer ignored him. After mugging dozens of people in the past, the fact that he was innocent of this particular crime was irrelevant.

He was released the next day. He thought about going to his sister's house, but he knew she would not believe him either. So he wrestled a purse away from its owner across the street from the courthouse, and went to Burger King.

He had nine legitimate arrests over the next three months. Once, the prosecutor made a half-hearted attempt to keep Silas in jail pending the earliest possible trial date. The public defender responded with a half-hearted plea for dismissal of the charges on some technicality. The judge could hardly contain her boredom. They all knew the county jail was overcrowded. And they all knew Silas would be around if they needed him. The judge asked him not to hurt anybody. In the plea negotiation the day before the twice-postponed trial date, the prosecutor held out for multiple convictions and consecutive sentences, almost a lifetime. Silas' lawyer did the best he could; two counts of assault with a deadly weapon and concurrent twenty-year sentences. His lawyer explained to him that Minnesota was cracking down on repeat offenders. He was going to the penitentiary for at least seven years.

Halfway through the seven years, Silas caught a break. It was his first.

The penitentiary had a half-time psychologist. (The entire prison population was his caseload, three hundred men, almost all of them disturbed.) The psychologist became aware of Silas and Silas' fanatic attachment to his walkman. A model prisoner otherwise, he became agitated when they took away or denied him permission to use the walkman. After one occasion when the prison store ran out of AA batteries, he bought extras and hoarded them in his cell against a reoccurrence. He wore the walkman whenever he was allowed to, even in his cell, and even in his sleep.

One day the psychologist noticed that Silas had little interest in the type of music most of the other young black men liked. He knew the radio reception in the cell-blocks was poor. He started wondering what it was Silas was listening to if not music. Talk Radio? Religious programming? He approached him during a recreation period.

"What are you listening to?"

"Nothin' much," said Silas.

"Music?"

"Not really."

"Let me listen a second."

"It's nothin', really. The reception ain't any good in here."

"Let me listen."

"No, really, there's nothin' on."

"I know. But I want to hear what it sounds like. I'll give it back."

Silas shrugged and handed his walkman to the psychologist. It was just static. Not very loud, but loud enough to be annoying. He checked the volume control. It was on high. The batteries must be dying. He fiddled with the tuning control. There was music here and there, but not where Silas had it set.

"Why don't you have it tuned to a station?"

"I don't know. There's never nothin' good on."

"Does the static help you think? Or not think about something you don't want to think about?"

"I guess."

"Which?"

"It helps me concentrate."

"On what?"

"I don't know, whatever."

"What do you hear when you're not wearing the walkman?"

"Folks don't say nothin' about it."

"No. I mean what do you hear in your head when no one is talking and you are not wearing your headphones?"

"I don't know. Just buzzing."

"Like the static on your radio?."

"Yeah, but different."

"Are there voices?"

"I guess."

"Are there distinct voices? Can you understand what they're saying?"

"Kinda."

"Do they tell you to do stuff?"

"No. They just talk."

"But they talk to you?"

"Sometimes."

"Do they talk about you?"

"Not really."

"You can understand the voices, they talk to you, but they don't tell you what to do or tell you that you are a bad person?"

"No."

"Do you recognize the voices? Is it anyone you know?"

Silas didn't answer right away. All these questions were making him nervous. He had seen this guy around but he didn't know why he asked so many questions. He had heard the guy referred to as the "cologist," but he had no idea what a "cologist" was.

"Who do the voices in your head belong to?"

"I don't know all of them. Not by name."

"But you know some of them?"

"I guess one of them is my uncle Leon."

"He is a real person then?"

"He was. He's dead now. He got shot up when I was little."

"What does he say?"

"Mostly he says he's gonna take me 'round."

"Around where?"

"I don't know."

"What does that mean, he's going to take you 'round?"

"Don't mean nothin'."

"Does he ever take you 'round?"

"Man, I told you he was dead! How's he gonna take me anywhere when I'm in prison and he's dead? Get away from me and stop asking me these fool questions. Ain't no sense talking to you."

The psychologist arranged to see Silas in his office the following week. Silas was not anxious to talk about the voices in his head, but at least it was a break from prison routine. Boredom was the very worst part of prison. He would have talked to anyone about anything to break the routine.

Between the two of them, they indexed the voices inside Silas' head: dead Uncle Leon, a cousin from Chicago, an elderly neighbor from Silas's youth, and two or three other, unidentified voices. One of the unidentified voices spoke to the uncle. The other voices spoke only to Silas. They said the same thing over and over; except the neighbor. He said two different things.

The uncle said he was gonna take Silas 'round. The cousin said he (the cousin) was gonna get his hair cut. The neighbor sometimes admonished Silas to stay out of his garden, and, at other times, talked about a catfish he (the neighbor) had caught down at the river. And so on. Nothing very important. Just the same stuff over and over. Silas heard them all the time. He couldn't really say when they started. Not when he was a child, but many years ago.

The prison did not have a psychiatrist, but there was a medical doctor who came two days a week. The psychologist and the M.D. collaborated on the psychiatric needs of the prisoners, of which there were many. They decided to try Haldol on Silas. A little Haldol had little effect. Silas complained slightly of dry mouth, but the voices were just as persistent. On a medium dose of Haldol, Silas complained greatly about his mouth being dry, and reported the voices unchanged. On a large dose of Haldol, the voices disappeared. Silas reported difficulty peeing, but he didn't mind too much. It was a great relief not to hear the voices all the time. He figured he would save a lot of money on batteries and sleep better without the cumbersome headset.

The psychologist contacted Silas' most recent attorney and advised him of the development. The attorney petitioned for Silas to be transferred to the state security hospital for the criminally insane at Shakopee. It took about a year to get the petition approved. (The officials in charge of such things had been burned before by convicts who pretended to be insane so they could do their time at the security hospital, which they thought would be cushier than the penitentiary.) The psychologist eventually convinced them that Silas was on the level. He really did hear voices and the Haldol really worked: classic indications of schizophrenia.

The psychiatrist at the hospital was horrified by the dosage of Haldol Silas was on. The dose was well beyond the recommended level for long-term maintenance. "This is exactly why only psychiatrists should be allowed to prescribe psychotropic medications," he thought to himself. He cut the dosage in half. The voices returned, but Silas didn't complain. He had lived with the voices for a long time and he was happy to be in the hospital instead of prison. Among other advantages at the hospital, he was allowed to wear his walkman, tuned to the static between stations, twenty-four hours a day. The return of the voices in his head was a minor annoyance.

The hospital was a lot less scary than prison, and there were more things to do: basketball, for example. In prison, there was an opportunity to play basketball once a week except that sometimes it got cancelled. But Silas never played because the guys on the court were bigger and faster than he was, and they made fun of him for trying to wear a walkman and play hoops at the same time. At the hospital there was an hour of indoor basketball three days a week, plus the chance to shoot baskets outside in the evening and on weekends. And nobody was as bulked-up and mean as they were in prison.

The hospital also had a deal called "group." A bunch of guys sat around in a room while some social worker talked to them. Silas hardly ever understood what the social worker talked about, and he didn't much care. He just waited out his time.

And after about a year they let him out. They sent him to a halfway house about a block from where he grew up, only six blocks from where his mother was living at the time. He thought it was heaven. He had a private room and he could lie around all day. The social workers had written up a plan for keeping an eye on him to make sure he didn't mug anyone, but the meals were good and they gave him spending money for an occasional Big Mac, so there was no reason to mug anyone. It was harder to get up a game than it had been in the hospital, but Silas could shoot baskets at the park whenever he wanted to.

And he could visit his mom. She was a lot nicer to him

now that he was a mental patient than she had been when he was a criminal. At first, he shot baskets and visited his mom quite frequently. As time went by, however, he did so less often. Eventually he gave up shooting baskets altogether. He still visited his mom once a week, but only if she called to remind him.

The people at the halfway house hooked him up with a psychiatrist. The psychiatrist thought the dosage of Haldol he had taken at the hospital was still too heavy so he cut it in half again. Silas continued to hear the voices.

Despite the voices and the reduced opportunity to play basketball, Silas was very happy at the halfway house. He would still be there now if they had allowed him to stay, but there was a twelve-month limit. As the limit approached, the staff of the halfway house and the county social worker despaired of what to do with Silas. Their general procedure was to teach people the basic skills for living alone and help them find an apartment. Silas had shown no interest in either. The halfway house staff considered him harmless and easy to get along with, but all he wanted to do was lie around and listen to his radio. It was hard to imagine Silas taking care of himself in an apartment.

At one point someone decided he should live with his mother, but his mother quickly and firmly said "no." Silas had lived with her off and on during his criminal career, and she had been unable to keep him out of trouble. She saw no reason to believe that anything would be different this time. She wanted him to get a job and be somebody. Couldn't they please make him do that?

The idea of a job seemed ridiculous to the halfway house staff, unless it was a job testing radios or mattresses. Keith, the county social worker, suggested a program run by Tasks Unlimited. People there lived in a small group, called a "lodge," and everybody had to work. Another client of his had been successful there.

The halfway house staff was against it. Some people who had flunked out of the Lodge Training Program had come through the halfway house following a subsequent hospitalization. They told horrible stories about Tasks. Reportedly, the staff there were obsessed with rules and the clients were like zombies. Everyone worked long hours at dreadful jobs and never had time for the kind of therapeutic activities which could produce personal growth. They made people go to work even when they were sick; one when he had a broken arm! The name, "Tasks Unlimited," said everything they needed to know.

Initially, these objections were reason enough to reject the Tasks Unlimited option. As the deadline approached, however, Silas' planning team became desperate. Silas refused to clean his room or wash his clothes or help make lunch. He wouldn't even bus his own dishes after meals. They had signed him up for Supplemental Security Income (S.S.I.), food stamps, a Section 8 housing voucher, and located some not-too-bad apartments which he could afford. But he was too lazy to even go look at the apartments.

Ultimately, the time limit left them no choice. They shook their heads and apologized to Silas for sending him to Tasks. The apologies made him slightly nervous. "How bad could it be?" he wondered.

His main concern was the food, and the Tasks Unlimited Lodge Training Program scored a big hit right away. The actual meals were about the same as the other halfway house, but there was a huge bonus; the kitchen was open all night!

The first night he was there, this guy named Ron asked out loud, "Does anybody want a pizza?" He wasn't speaking directly to Silas, so Silas didn't say anything, but another guy said, "Yeah," and stood up. When the two of them headed off toward the kitchen, Silas followed them to see what would happen.

They went into the kitchen, which wasn't locked, opened
the freezer, which wasn't locked, took out a frozen pizza and put
it in the oven. And they weren't through. Ron said he wanted
extra cheese. So he opened the refrigerator, which wasn't locked,
took out a big hunk of cheese, and started cutting it up. After a
while, he took the half-cooked pizza out of the oven, put the
cheese on top of it, and put it back in the oven.

The whole time, Silas stood in the kitchen doorway. The
two pizza-makers knew he was there, but they waited for him to
say something. Silas grew increasingly curious to see if the pizza
would get cooked before the staff caught them. He didn't hang
in the doorway because he was afraid of being caught; he had
been caught too often to worry about that. There just didn't
seem to be any advantage to joining the crime scene until the
pizza was done. When the pizza was ready, Ron took three
plates out of the cupboard. Silas didn't wait to find out who the
third plate was for; he sat down next to the others and took two
big slices for himself. He ate his fast, not knowing when the staff
would show up.

He later learned that their late-evening snack wasn't even
against the rules. Some food items were marked "save for
Thursday dinner," or whatever, but you could get a snack whenever you wanted. Especially something called "leftovers."
Leftovers were a whole new concept to Silas.

After he got to know Ron better, Silas told him how much
he liked hamburgers. Ron came up with a scheme which
involved ordering more ground beef than they really needed for
a meal, and then not using it all. Automatic leftovers!

Ron would cook Silas a hamburger whenever he wanted
one. Ron didn't sleep much, so even if Silas woke up hungry
(whenever he woke up, he was hungry) in the middle of the
night, Ron would cook him a hamburger. Silas thought it was a
pretty sweet deal until one day Ron just disappeared. Didn't tell

anybody he was leaving, least of all Silas.

None of the other residents, "trainees" they were called, was interested in cooking Silas hamburgers in the middle of the night. The staff told him he could make his own hamburgers, but even though he had watched Ron and the people at McDonald's make hundreds of them, he didn't know how. With a little practice, he figured out how to make a pop-tart. They weren't as tasty as a hamburger, but they were easier to make.

The bad part about the Lodge Training Program was the work. Well, not the work itself; even though it was his first job in his whole life, it wasn't that hard. The problem was, Ray wouldn't let him wear his walkman when he worked. "Doesn't look professional," Ray said. The first few days Ray made him take it off but let him keep it with him. As soon as Ray was out of his face he put it back on. By the end of the first week, Ray wouldn't let him take it to the work site at all.

Silas' attachment to the walkman came to Dr. Bob's attention. He started asking Silas about the voices in his head as though he knew all about them. Every week Dr. Bob would ask him about the voices, and, regardless of what Silas said, the doctor would increase his Haldol. Eventually he was taking the same dosage he had taken when in prison, and the voices went away. At first, he continued to wear the walkman whenever he wasn't working. But with the voices gone, and people hassling him about the walkman, he wore it less and less.

Silas had never been much of a conversationalist, and in all the years he wore a walkman, people didn't talk much to him. Sometimes someone would say something to him and he would just grunt or maybe say something which didn't quite make sense. It seemed as though having a conversation with him would require a great deal of effort on the other person's part. Except for his mother, people usually didn't try that hard.

As he wore the walkman less, however, people made more of an effort to talk to him. Silas still wasn't much of a talker, but he turned out to be a great listener. He listened, even paid attention, when other people talked about themselves, which was what most of them wanted to talk about. Having little personal experience with the mental health system, he found their stories fascinating and they sure enjoyed talking about themselves.

They had "group" at the Lodge Training Program also. Silas still didn't like it much. One day, during group, the social worker asked the trainees to write down the name of their best friend in the program. Silas found the task difficult. His late-night hamburger cook, Ron, was long gone; so was James, who had been the only other black person in the group. The crazy white people were okay, but he hadn't thought of any of them as friends. He half decided on Terry, but he wasn't sure how to spell "Terry." So at the last minute he wrote down "BOB."

Every other member of the group wrote down "SILAS."

Silas' popularity continued after he graduated from training and joined the Spirit Lodge. He was such a wonderful listener that over time, every Spirit and a couple of guys from other lodges came to regard him as their best friend. He also became famous for his skill in making cheeseburgers.

*"There is nothing about
a Board of Directors in
Fairweather's book."*

Chris Nielsen
Spirit Lodge

CHAPTER EIGHT

ON A MISSION
FROM GOD

Chris was down at the lake one afternoon, lying in the grass
watching some clouds roll by. Most were typical cloud shaped,
but one was very odd. As he looked closer, he suddenly realized
it wasn't a cloud at all. It was an angel! As he watched in
astonishment, the angel floated slowly down and hovered
just a foot or two above him.

"Chris," said the angel, pronouncing his name in a peculiar
manner. With a long "I" like "Christ" without the "T."

"What?" he said.

"What are you doing with your life?"

"What should I be doing?"

"There's a lot to do. You are part of His plan."

"God's plan?"

"Of course."

"I don't know what to do."

"Of course you do."

"Will you help me?"

"Of course."

According to Chris, he was never quite the same after his encounter with the angel. He had suspected for some time that there had to be some special purpose in his life, but he didn't know what it was. He still didn't. He wondered if he might be Christ. Why would the angel call him "Chris" (as rhymes with "rice") instead of "Chris" (as rhymes with "miss")? On the other hand, if he were Christ, why wouldn't the angel just call him "Christ" instead of "Chris"? Was it all some sort of puzzle he was supposed to solve?

He didn't tell anyone about his encounter with the angel; not his parents, nor his friends, nor his study group. They wouldn't understand. He spent the next few weeks trying to understand his special mission. At first he thought about it all the time. He couldn't study; his boss yelled at him for not paying attention to his work. As the weeks went by, still without a definitive answer to the puzzle, he forced himself to think about other things.

He was driving home from school, thinking about the Gopher basketball game that evening. He was stopped at a light. A car pulled up next to him and the driver rolled down his window to say something. The other driver looked familiar, but Chris couldn't place the face at first. The other driver said something, but Chris didn't understand it. The other driver gave him a funny look and drove away when the light turned green. As he did, it hit Chris who he was. It was that guy "Bone," Deb's other boyfriend!

Jealous rage surged through Chris' veins. He punched the accelerator to the floor. Bone had gotten a head start while Chris tried to figure out who he was, but Chris closed the gap in a hurry. Bone's car was traveling about thirty and Chris' about fifty when he rammed him from the rear. Both cars spun out of control. Chris' car jumped a curb, glanced off a tree, and slammed sideways into a building. Bone's came to a stop in the opposite lane of traffic, but fortunately no one hit him. And it wasn't really Bone, just some guy who looked vaguely like him.

According to his parents, Chris was never quite the same again after the "accident." The police took him to jail. They saw the bumps on his head and offered him medical attention, but he declined. After bailing him out, his parents tried to take him to the emergency room, but he wouldn't go. Although he had no experience with the mental health system up to that point, he had a sense, a voice in his head maybe, that a doctor would think he was crazy. The voice of the angel had been particularly active during the hours he spent in jail with the bumps on his head.

At the time of the accident, Chris was in his second year of medical school at the University of Minnesota. He was doing fine, absorbing the material easily and scoring well on his exams. Shortly after the accident, however, he began to have difficulty concentrating. He was okay in his room or an isolated corner of the library, but he found himself easily distracted by movement or noise, and the voice of the angel had returned.

His fellow med students were increasingly a distraction. Especially one, who called herself "Diane." Diane was a large woman, at least five-foot-ten and at least 175 pounds. She was muscular and verbally aggressive. She wanted to be a surgeon. She had an unusually high voice, however, and some exaggerated feminine mannerisms. When she walked, for example, she took dainty little steps and held her hands, palm down, perpendicularly out from her thighs, as though she were a very young girl tiptoeing through the flowers.

Chris became convinced that Diane was a man in woman's clothing. He knew this because whenever Diane was around, he heard the angel's voice saying "Dave." Obviously, "Diane's" real name was "Dave."

Chris became increasingly distracted by Dave/Diane. His/her presence in their midst was an abomination. He was convinced that everyone else knew Dave/Diane was a man; it was perfectly obvious. But no one else would say anything because they didn't understand how terribly wrong it was. When he couldn't stand it any longer, he spoke up in his cellular biology seminar, "How long are we going to sit here in the presence of a man dressed as a woman and act like nothing is wrong?" Everyone acted as if they didn't know what he was talking about. He pointed at Diane, "His real name is Dave."

There was an embarrassed silence. No one knew what to say, least of all Diane. One of the other female students finally told Chris to shut up. The professor said they had a lot of ground to cover before the next exam, and no time for nonsense. At the end of the class, the professor told Chris to stay and speak with him. The professor asked what he could possibly be thinking. Chris explained the obvious: the masculine characteristics, the pseudo-femininity. He didn't mention how he knew her name was "Dave." The professor described the theory as ridiculous and offensive. He advised Chris to keep his "crackpot theories" to himself from now on.

He did not; he felt compelled to speak out against such an abomination. Since the faculty wouldn't listen, he lectured his fellow students on the dangers of homosexuality and the insult to decency of Dave/Diane's charade. Diane was too embarrassed to complain, but several of her classmates were not.

Chris' advisor called him in for a visit. The purpose of the visit was to inform Chris of his immediate suspension from medical school. The advisor asked Chris if he was doing drugs. Chris insisted he was not. The advisor wished him well and said he could apply for reinstatement when he "got his act together."

Chris did not immediately tell his parents about being thrown out of med school or losing his part-time job. He kept leaving in the morning as if going to school, and coming home late at night. Too late in his mother's opinion, but Chris explained that he was studying.

Chris was listening to his angel and experimenting with life on the streets, among the homeless and the forlorn. He now felt that his still mysterious mission was connected to homelessness. Somehow he had to save the homeless; whether spiritually or economically, he wasn't certain. He assumed he would receive further instructions from the angel when the time was right. The angel didn't exactly tell him to become homeless, or even to associate with the homeless; it just made sense. The more familiar he was with homelessness, the better prepared he would be when his mission became clear.

At first he merely visited the streets. As he became more comfortable on the streets, he began to view the streets as his true home. He dropped by his parents' house on occasion to eat or clean up a little, but he felt guilty afterwards. His new friends on the street didn't have the opportunity to eat or clean up.

He became increasingly critical of his parents and their friends. Why did they deserve to have so much when others had so little. He knew his parents gave generously to charities. And he knew his mother had worked tirelessly, sometimes at risk to her own health and safety, for causes intended to equalize wealth. But in the end, his parents drank fine wine in a fourteen-room house while his new friends drank Thunderbird in abandoned grain elevators. It just wasn't right.

Chris became increasingly abusive toward his parents. He ate meals at home when he could (he had no money), but he wouldn't eat with his parents. They tried to ask him about med school, but every conversation with them led to his angry denunciation of their lifestyle. His father, Ed, made some calls and confirmed what he had begun to suspect; Chris had dropped out of school. After a particularly difficult weekend, they confronted him and he admitted it. But he would not explain, and turned the conversation back to their lifestyle. They were at the end of their rope. His mother, Marge, finally agreed to a solution Ed had proposed weeks before. They threw their son out of their home. It was a very difficult decision for Ed and Marge, but they didn't know what else to do.

After a week on the street, without eating or sleeping regularly, the angel confirmed what Chris had suspected all along. He was Christ! His mission was to end world hunger.

The hunger problem was surprisingly easy to solve; in fact, the solutions were common knowledge in the scientific community. Despite runaway population growth, there was plenty of food, much of which went to waste. If food production, storage and distribution systems operated at peak efficiency, there was no reason for anyone to go hungry. Greed and indifference were the only problems. His mission was to call public attention to the need to act.

And he knew just how to do it. He panhandled enough money to buy a ticket to a Minnesota Twins game which he mistakenly thought was being televised nationally. He sneaked down into the box seats, and at a crucial point in the eighth inning, he took all his clothes off and ran out onto the field.

He more or less expected the police to come out and try to grab him, but he didn't think they would be able to drag him off as quickly as they did. He felt that something, he wasn't sure what, would prevent his immediate arrest. Surely the crowd, or the players, or the cops would demand an explanation.

"Stop! Wait! Listen to him," someone would yell. "Find out what he has to say."

He didn't even know what he was going to say. He assumed his friend the angel would help him when the time came.

Moving through the stadium tunnels in custody afterwards, he explained to the police what his plan had been, and how surprised he was that it had not worked. They decided to skip the standard booking procedure and take him directly to the county psych ward.

When the hospital was ready to discharge him, Ed and Marge stuck by their decision not to let him come home, even though his condition had improved. The hospital social worker talked to him about halfway house options; one of them was the lodge training program run by Tasks Unlimited.

Almost immediately after graduating to the Spirit Lodge, Chris was chosen as the lodge's Social Chair. The main duties of this position were to represent Spirit Lodge at monthly planning meetings with the Social Chairs from all the other lodges. He came to enjoy planning all-lodge events: anniversary recognitions, summer picnics, etc. And he took the initiative to set up smaller activities, such as the Spirit and Hiawatha Lodges going out for pizza after work.

Later, the nominally paid position of All-Lodge Rec Assistant opened up. Tasks had a half-time social worker, Pam, who served as the Recreation Coordinator for the whole agency. Susie from the Lilacs had been the Assistant, but she was dying of cancer. Chris applied for the Rec Assistant position and was hired.

He was effective in improving the all-lodge rec program. For example, Pam was not particularly enthusiastic about weekend activities as she preferred not to work weekends. Chris began to change all this. He promoted the idea of a least one recreation activity every weekend, even if it was just going out to eat. He promoted the idea of other Tasks' staff besides Pam attending weekend activities. Pam was reluctant to ask salaried staff to attend things on their own time, especially if she wasn't going to be there herself, but Chris was not reluctant. And he especially promoted the idea that rec activities could be successful without staff. As activities became less staff dependent, staff felt the activities were less like work, so they came on their own time more often.

Another example was related to the fact that some lodge members were disabled by their mental illness less obviously than others. They were self-conscious about appearing in public in a large group which included their embarrassingly disabled lodgemates. So Chris organized smaller and more sophisticated activities like canoe trips and attending live theatre. If a group of three or four athletic members wanted to play basketball or volleyball, Chris encouraged them to go to a community center and join an adult pickup game where they would have to play against people more skilled than they were rather than in the "everybody plays whether they know how or not" atmosphere of the all-lodge games.

And Chris was the inspiration for another major development.

About two-thirds of Tasks lodge members went to their families for major holidays like Thanksgiving and Christmas. But that left twenty-five or thirty who didn't, mostly because they didn't have any family. Or maybe they weren't invited. Some of the people who did get invited would invite a friend along, but that still left one or two people per lodge with nowhere to go. They stayed home and ate by themselves, or maybe went out to eat with one other person. Most said they didn't mind being alone on holidays, but Chris minded. With Marge's permission, he invited everyone to his parents' house.

The first year, Marge served fourteen lodge members on Thanksgiving, and eleven on Christmas. The second year, it was eighteen and sixteen. Marge's generosity was ample, but she was running out of seating, even in her Lake of the Isles mansion.

Chris had joined a Lutheran Church near the Spirit Lodge. He attended faithfully and knew the pastor well. When holiday dinners began to outgrow his parents' home, he arranged to hold them at his church. The church's only condition was that they clean up afterwards, and the lodge folks were professional cleaners.

Chris had intended that he and his mother would do most of the cooking. Lodge members would bring a salad or dessert to share. But Lois, from Hiawatha Lodge, volunteered to take charge of the cooking. Lois was famous for her meals at Hiawatha Lodge; no one was ever late for dinner when it was her turn to cook.

The event grew and grew. Calvin from the Painters, who used to eat alone with his father, and Dean from the Spirits, who used to eat alone with his mother, asked if they could bring their parents. Dale from Hiawatha brought his two unmarried sisters and their four kids.

Especially on Thanksgiving, smaller families without a lot of in-law connections started attending the lodge event at Chris' church, in lieu of inviting their lodge-living relatives to their house. Tasks Unlimited Building Services paid for the food, Pam helped Chris coordinate the transportation, and lots of people pitched in to help Lois cook. Eventually they were serving around sixty on Thanksgiving and around forty on Christmas.

Chris really liked the idea of providing a real Christmas for folks who otherwise would not have had one. He felt it was a part of the mission for which he had been sent. In addition to eating a great meal and exchanging presents, he insisted on recognition of the religious aspects of Christmas. Chris knew that some of the staff were timid about mentioning Christ at official Tasks' functions, but he wasn't.

He talked about God, and his special relationship to God whenever he could. And Christmas, he felt, was certainly one of those times, even though Warren and a couple of the other lodge members were Jewish.

Lodges had been designed in the first place by a guy named Fairweather. Chris had read two of Fairweather's books since joining the Spirit Lodge. Fairweather Lodges were supposed to be run by recovering mental patients for the benefit of recovering mental patients. Chris thought the staff at Tasks sometimes forgot for whose benefit the lodges had been created, and they certainly forgot by whom the lodges were meant to be run.

Mark, the lodge coordinator at the Spirit Lodge, pretty much let the members make the day-to-day decisions, such as what to have for dinner or whether to buy HBO on their cable. Bigger decisions, such as buying a new lodge van or deciding how many members to have in Spirit Lodge, were more heavily influenced by staff. Mark always said the ultimate decision was theirs, but they had to "run it by" the Tasks Unlimited Board of Directors.

There was nothing in Fairweather's books about a Board of Directors reviewing their decisions. The lodge was supposed to be smart enough to make their own decisions, and strong enough to live with their mistakes. When he first heard there was a Tasks Unlimited Board of Directors, Chris demanded to know who was on it. He was reassured to learn that there were actual lodge residents on the board, and some ex-residents as well, but frustrated to learn there was no current Spirit on the board. He demanded to know why not.

"There are too many lodges for each lodge to have their own board representative," Mark explained.

"Why?"

"I don't know. There are just too many."

"Every lodge has a representative on the all-lodge recreation council," Chris pointed out.

"That's different."

"How?"

"The Board of Directors makes really big decisions."

"Like what?"

"Like when to buy a new van."

"So what do they know about when we should buy a new van?"

"Well, its really a lodge's decision; the Board of Directors merely reviews it."

"But how can they 'review' our decision if they don't know anything about it in the first place?"

"Why are you hassling me about it? I don't make the rules around here. I don't know how it works. Talk to one of the lodge members on the board, like Trevor from the Painters, or Judy from the Lilacs."

So he talked to Trevor about it. Trevor agreed to submit his name to the nominating committee, and Chris was elected to the Board of Directors of Tasks Unlimited. He was very proud to be elected; this also felt like part of his mission on earth.

Serving on the board, however, was somewhat of a disappointment. The board was the ultimate authority over everything at Tasks Unlimited, and he was a full voting member, but it was boring. The primary topic at board meetings was finance, which sounded exciting at first, but it really wasn't. The income was fixed, and the expenses were fixed, and everything came out even. But the board talked about it anyway, for hours on end.

At first, Chris had ideas for new projects or improvements which would cost money. One of the board members would shake his head gravely and ask, "How can we afford that?" Or, "What should we not do instead?" Chris would study the

budget in front of him and conclude it was impossible. Tasks
had lots of money, but only for what they were already doing.
And if it didn't cost money, the board didn't have time for it.

He attended the meetings faithfully, but it wasn't as fulfilling as he thought it would be.

He turned his attention back to the recreation situation. The
more he thought about it, he could not understand why he was
the Rec Assistant reporting to the staff Rec Coordinator. He
didn't mind that Pam made more money than he did; he didn't
like needing to get her approval for everything.

Pam had a Bachelor of Arts Degree from Minneapolis
Community College; hardly the equivalent of his pre-med
degree from Princeton. The only justification for Pam's position
of authority seemed to be that she had never personally experienced psychiatric difficulties. Could it be that Tasks Unlimited,
supposedly created for the benefit of people with mental illness,
was actually discriminating against him? While he was mulling
this over, however, Pam quit to raise a family.

"No way this could be a coincidence," Chris told the Spirits.
"Becoming the Rec Coordinator is the next step on my mission."

He proposed at a Tasks board meeting that he become the
new Rec Coordinator. The board said it was up to the director.
The director said they could discuss it after the meeting. After
the meeting, the director said they had already run an ad in the
paper, but Chris could apply just like anyone else. Chris did,
and the director called him in for an interview. "Just like everyone else," he said.

"Why do you want to be the Recreation Coordinator?"
the director asked him.

Chris was shocked by the question. "Why would you ask
a question like that?" he demanded.

"Well, ... uh," said the director.

"The angel told me to," said Chris. He went on to explain how he might actually be Christ, and how becoming the Rec Coordinator of Tasks Unlimited was surely part of his special mission.

The director seemed to take this rather matter-of-factly. He made a couple of notes on his pad of paper. Chris found this unnerving. "What do you consider your strengths and weaknesses for this position?" he asked next.

Chris was doubly shocked. "Why are you asking about the minor mistakes I've made? Why do you insist on focusing on the negative? If you don't want to hire me just say so."

He didn't get the job. He felt he had been tricked into talking about the angel in his head.

Chris had grown up on the shores of Lake of the Isles, Minneapolis' toniest lake. His father, Ed, was a prominent urologist with a faculty post at the University Medical School as well as a thriving private practice. His mother, Marge, was a political activist who worked tirelessly on a succession of left-wing causes. Together with her neighbor, Rosie, a professor of political science, they were infamous as the "Lake of the Isles Liberals."

The two of them achieved great notoriety, for example, for their campaign to have Marxism taught in the public schools as a viable alternative theory to capitalism. Rosie thought that college was too late to introduce students to Marx, and Marge, conveniently, had an undergraduate degree in elementary education.

So they developed a K-12 curriculum which incorporated Marxist theory into reading, arithmetic, and natural science instruction, as a counter balance to what they considered the pervasive capitalist propaganda. They never prevailed in having their curriculum adopted by the Minneapolis school system, but they came as close as a three-to-two vote.

Rosie was Marge's best friend; she had seemed like a second mother to Chris when he was growing up. Since his return from college and the onset of his illness, however, their relationship had changed. She was much less judgmental about his erratic behavior than his mother. And even though she shared his parents' limousine-liberal lifestyle, she was much more interested in Chris' theory that it was wrong to have fourteen rooms when other people have none. Whereas he often thought of his mother as a hypocrite despite her tireless efforts on behalf of various left-wing causes, Rosie's commitment to these causes seemed somehow more sincere. Despite their eighteen year age difference, Chris was very attracted to Rosie.

So when Rosie and Marge announced they were organizing a trip to Cuba, Chris signed on immediately.

It was an easy cause to get into. According to Rosie and Marge's literature, the innocent peasants of Cuba were dying prematurely of diseases easily cured or prevented with modern medicine — all because of a thirty-year-old political dispute of which they had little understanding.

Chris threw himself into the project. He distributed information about the upcoming trip to medical and nursing students at the University, to medical personnel at the County Hospital where he had been a patient, and even throughout the lodge program. He succeeded in recruiting a third-year med student, a nursing student, a pre-med student, his favorite nurse from the county psych ward, a retired social worker from the Tasks Unlimited Board, and Carl of the Diamond Lodge, who had worked for two years as a hospital orderly. The rest of the twelve member team included himself, his parents and Rosie, an experienced pediatrician and a professor of pharmacology.

They spent two weeks in Cuba, mostly in the regional capital of Camaguey. The Communist authorities and local hospital staff were all extremely cooperative. Whatever the reality of the political causes and effects, the ailing members of the community really needed the help Chris' team provided. They inoculated babies and young children and treated all kinds of adult diseases, especially bowel and bladder infections.

Chris worked all day and made love to Rosie all night (but only in his dreams). When he confessed his love to Rosie she acknowledged that she loved him too, but a sexual relationship was out of the question under the circumstances. They would have to be platonic lovers.

He worked like a dog, carrying and organizing equipment and supplies, sterilizing reusable tools, disposing of contaminated material, cleaning up, and running errands. He got winded in the Cuban heat, so unlike the Minnesota weather they had left behind, but Chris never let on. How could he complain when the sick were silent?

He was embarrassed when he thought about the low level of understanding among Minnesotans of how well they, even lodge members, lived in comparison to the rest of the world. Folks living in lodges lived in splendor compared to the average Cuban. He knew that some people outside the lodge looked down on the janitorial work the lodge members did, but he saw how hard the Cubans worked for so much less. He learned that the nurses and other skilled medical workers at the Camaguey clinic were paid only a fraction of what the average Tasks Unlimited janitor earned. And the clinic's only doctor earned less than Everett, the crew chief from the Hiawatha Lodge.

His mission suddenly became clear.

His role was to raise consciousness about the affluence which people took for granted. He knew others had tried this, but the mistake they generally made was to direct their efforts at the rich. This wouldn't work because the rich didn't get it. Chris' parents and their friends, for example, (Rosie, a Marxist, was an exception) thought they were rich because they deserved to be rich. Chris concluded that Christ had not preached to the rich because he knew the rich were hopeless; he preached to the poor because they were the only ones with the capacity to understand!

Chris would take this message to the lodge members — to teach them how lucky they were to have nice homes, and good jobs, and each other — especially each other. Lodge folks, who had overcome illnesses such as schizophrenia and chronic depression to build a decent life for themselves, were the ones to teach the rest of the world how to live.

As much as he enjoyed the two weeks in Cuba, he could hardly wait to get back to Minnesota to get started.

"Jan kind of gives retirement a bad name."

Lois Bjorge
Hiawatha Lodge

CHAPTER NINE

FROM FARM
TO LODGE

Lois doesn't need a recipe to cook Chicken Paprika; it is one of her specialties. The hard part is finding the ingredients. Lois can't make Chicken Paprika without the paprika.

Jan's constant pantry reorganization is the problem. Lois makes Chicken Paprika about once a month; she would fix it every week if it were up to Ed and Everett. Occasionally Lois will make Chicken Paprika twice within Jan's four-week cycle of cleaning and reorganizing the pantry, in which case the can of paprika will be right where she left it. But it doesn't often work out that way.

Sometimes Lois can spot the pattern right away, and find the paprika neatly between the pancake mix and the paraffin (neither pandowdy nor papayas being a standard part of the Hiawathan diet), but mostly not. Paprika could turn up with the spicy food, the red food, or perhaps food consumed in some old black and white movie only Jan has seen.

In Lois' mind, Jan gives retirement a bad name, but at least she does the dishes. At other lodges, whoever cooks does the dishes, which Lois would not like because it holds down the number of courses people serve. At Hiawatha Lodge, Lois can serve soup and salad and two kinds of vegetables (assuming they are peas and string beans, the only vegetables the Hiawathans will eat) and dessert (no problem there) and Jan will clean it all up.

Hiawatha Lodge has the world's cleanest kitchen. Jan washes the dishes, sends out the garbage, cleans the counter tops, sweeps and mops the floor twice a day, and changes Lovey's litter box twice a week. She cleans the refrigerator, the stainless steel and the porcelain once a day. She cleans the light fixture, the windows, and wipes down the walls and the cabinets twice a week. Jan cleans the oven once a week. She used to clean the oven every day, but Alex, the Lodge Coordinator, said the coating on the inside of the oven was wearing off and then the oven wouldn't heat evenly. Jan dusts the refrigerator coils every other week and every four weeks she defrosts the freezer. The Hiawathans had discussed purchasing a frost-free model but dropped the idea when Lois pointed out that Jan would defrost it anyway.

And every four weeks, on a schedule opposite that of the defrosting, Jan cleans the pantry. To Jan, cleaning the pantry means emptying every drawer and every shelf in every cupboard, wiping everything down, replacing any torn or stained shelf paper, taking complete inventory, making a detailed list of items to be restocked at the weekly shopping, and reorganizing everything according to her latest scheme.

Jan grew up on a farm; you can see it in her hands. Five-three and barely a hundred pounds, she has hands like a gorilla. Cover her hands and she looks the frail old woman of seventy which she is. Her hands look as though they belong on a man, hands that could take a tractor apart without a wrench.

Jan hasn't lived on the farm full time since her mother died when she was twenty-two. Until then, Jan worked every day in the garden with her mom, or in the fields with her dad, Vernon, and her two brothers, Mike and Nick. They worked from sunrise to sundown seven days a week. Jan loved the farm and all the animals, but her brothers picked on her a lot, always teasing her about how she ought to be getting married.

In 1952, Jan's mother caught pneumonia and died. A couple of weeks later Vernon told Jan that she was going to have to marry his friend Jake. Jan refused. Later, Vernon told her to pack up some things, he was taking her to see a doctor in Mendota and they might need to stay overnight. Jan said she wasn't sick, but Vernon said they would let the doctor decide. Jan wondered why her dad thought she was sick, and why they were driving all the way to Mendota when there were doctors in their town.

Mendota turned out to be the state psychiatric hospital, and Jan didn't even see a doctor until the third day. When they first got there, Vernon went into an office to talk to somebody while Nick and Jan sat in the waiting room. When he came out, Vernon told Jan she would have to stay a few days "for observation." Nick helped Jan unload her stuff out of the truck, then Nick and Vernon both hugged her and drove away. They had to get home in time to help Mike with the milking.

The doctor told Jan she had paranoid schizophrenia, for which there was no cure. She would have to stay at Mendota for a while to see if her condition improved. Jan didn't understand how whatever it was would improve if they didn't have a cure. They gave her a medication called Thorazine, but true to the doctor's word, it did not cure her schizophrenia.

Jan missed her mom, but other than that, Mendota wasn't too bad. Mendota had its own farm. One hundred and eighty acres of corn and hay, eighteen milkers (almost like home) and the biggest vegetable garden Jan had ever seen. Jan quickly became one of the hospital's best gardeners. Jan loved gardening for several reasons, one of which was that it gave her something to do seven days a week. Some of the patients went to therapy instead of working, but there was no therapy on weekends so they had nothing to do on Saturday and Sunday.

As long as Vernon was alive, Jan was sent on home visits two or three times a year. She enjoyed visiting her home place, because even without her mom there, things felt familiar. But by the time Vernon died, Mike's two little boys were using Jan's old room and Mike's wife Cathy was pregnant again, so there wasn't much room for Jan anyway.

One day, the Mendota farm foreman told Jan and the others that they would not be raising any more vegetables, just a few flowers. And they were selling off the dairy herd also. It seemed that someone at the State Capitol in Saint Paul had decided, based on an article he read in *The New York Times*, that having the patients at the state hospital grow their own vegetables and produce their own dairy products was cruel and inhumane. The farm foreman and a couple of the nurses wanted to go to Saint Paul to argue about it, but the head of the hospital said it wouldn't do any good. The herd was sold and the farm shut down.

For about six years, Jan didn't have anything much to do.
There was a place patients could go to make things out of
leather, but by the time she had made two belts, two purses, and
a pair of moccasins she never wore, she lost interest in leather.

Sometimes Jan would ask the doctor about her schizophrenia and if they had found a cure yet. The doctor said he would
be sure to tell Jan when they did. One day a nurse asked Jan if
she wanted to join a new program called "Fairweather." Jan
figured it would involve being outside, especially in the summer,
so she signed up right away. Turned out, the Fairweather group
spent all their time indoors, sweeping and mopping. Jan didn't
like janitorial work as well as gardening, but it was a lot better
than sitting around.

Two years later, they sent Jan and the other patients she had
been working with to live in a house in Minneapolis. Before the
Hiawathans left the state hospital, they signed a pledge to stay at
least one year. All nine of them did. A man named John didn't
like it at first and insisted on going back to the hospital, but then
he changed his mind and came back again.

Over time, all of the original Hiawathans except Jan moved
on. As they did, Tasks would find replacements, and after a few
years they would move on too. Some would move to other
lodges, some out on their own. Di was the second-to-last of the
original Hiawathans. Di had been a Hiawathan for twelve years
until she got into a bitter argument with one of the new girls,
took all her stuff and moved out in the middle of the night.
Jan, on the other hand, got along pretty well with everybody.
The only lodge members Jan didn't like were guys who tried to
boss her around. But the guys who started out bossy usually got
taken down a notch or two by the whole group.

Hiawatha Lodge was a nicer place to live than the state hospital, and much fancier than the farm house she grew up in. And they had cats; just like on the farm. But the thing Jan liked best about it was the work. The Hiawathans all worked as janitors. Initially the lodge operated their own separate janitorial business. Later on, Tasks created a janitorial corporation all the members of all the lodges could work for if they liked. Jan and the other Hiawathans liked. Tasks was able to get better contracts than the Hiawathans had ever had; the work was steadier, four hours a day, five days a week, fifty-two weeks a year.

Jan worked hard around the house also. The Hiawathans took turns cooking and washing dishes, but Jan was in charge of cleaning the kitchen weekly. She cleaned it twice a week just to be safe. Jan was also in charge of raising the peas and string beans. Other Hiawathans had special jobs like managing the lodge checkbook, supervising everybody else's meds, or driving the Hiawatha van. Jan could add and subtract and she had been driving since she was ten, but she didn't like paperwork or city traffic, so she stuck to the kitchen and the garden.

While Jan was at Mendota, waiting for a cure for schizophrenia, the doctor told her she had diabetes. As luck would have it, there wasn't a cure for that either. So in addition to Thorazine, Jan took insulin every day. Jan's schizophrenia wasn't curable, but at least it didn't get any worse, at least not as far as Jan could tell and the doctor never said different. But the diabetes got worse. After about ten years at Hiawatha Lodge, the doctor said Jan would have to have insulin injections every day instead of taking pills. A public health nurse taught Jan how to give herself the injection.

Eventually, the diabetes affected Jan's circulation. She got an infection on her right foot and it wouldn't heal. The doctor tried everything, but the infection continued to grow, and after a

few months it started up her leg. Doctor Bob sent Jan to a
specialist who decided Jan's leg would have to be amputated
right below the knee.

Jan wasn't happy losing a leg, but even less happy about
going to the hospital. Her only prior hospital experience was at
Mendota, where they kept her eighteen years. By now, she had
lived at Hiawatha Lodge for twenty-one years and become kind
of attached to a routine of working as a janitor twenty hours a
week, cleaning the kitchen twice a week, and cooking once a
week. She didn't want to go back to the hospital.

When Jan was admitted to the hospital, they wanted to
know about her insurance. Alex, the Coordinator helped Jan
explain that Tasks Unlimited Building Services provided hospitalization only to full time employees. Since Jan received Social
Security Disability, she was eligible to purchase Medicare for a
few dollars each month, but Jan had steadfastly refused. So, no,
Jan did not have insurance.

The woman at the hospital said they had a special program
for indigents. Jan didn't recognize the term; Alex said Jan wasn't
one. The woman said the bill might run as high as $12,000 or
$15,000. Alex said Jan would pay it; Jan said she would cut the
leg off herself. But before she went in for the operation, Alex
drove Jan to the bank where she got a money order for $14,000.
Almost half of the $30,000 she had saved up while at Hiawatha
Lodge.

Jan was sixty-one when she lost her leg. They gave her a
plastic one, but it never worked well enough for her to do much
walking, which ended her career as a janitor. Darcy, the social
worker, talked Jan's brother, Mike, into inviting Jan to live on the
farm, at least on a trial basis. She also located two nursing
homes, one near the farm and one in Minneapolis. She asked
Jan what she wanted to do.

Jan said she wanted a ground floor bedroom at Hiawatha Lodge. Jan explained to the Hiawathans that although she couldn't work with the crew, she could do plenty of stuff around the house. Washing dishes and kitchen cleaning had been a rotating job which no one wanted. Jan offered to do kitchen duty everyday, three hundred and sixty five days a year. Jan also offered to cook every third day, which would reduce everyone else's cooking responsibility.

Lois agreed to switch bedrooms with her. And except for Dale who didn't like Jan's tater-tot hot dish, the Hiawathans quickly agreed. Even Dale went along with Alex's suggestion that they cut Jan's lodge dues in half. Alex said the Hiawatha Lodge was in good financial shape and could cut Jan some slack without needing to increase anyone else's dues. Everett pointed out that the Hiawathans wouldn't get any dues from an empty bed, and any replacement for Jan, especially a young man, would probably eat more than Jan.

The Hiawathans voted six to zero to keep Jan on as a retired member at half-dues. Alex said Jan should have abstained from the vote, but it was a moot point.

It's been nine years since Jan retired. She keeps the cleanest kitchen in town and reorganizes the pantry every four weeks. She cooks every third day, and has expanded her repertoire to include chili and lasagna. Dale complained loud enough about tater-tot hot dish that Alex got Darcy to teach Jan some new menus.

Jan's finances have worked out okay. Darcy got her into a program which pays eighty percent of the cost of her Thorazine and insulin. Some of the younger members blow their money on all kinds of foolishness, but not Jan. She hasn't touched her life savings in years. Jan's Social Security is enough to cover the co-payments for her medications, her rent to Tasks, and half-dues to Hiawatha Lodge.

The most unsettling event in Jan's retirement was the trouble between Max and Lovey. Max was only ten weeks old when he joined Hiawatha Lodge, and playful as a kitten can be. He was silvery grey and white, and loved to play in paper bags and chase ping-pong balls.

Fourteen-year-old Lovey tolerated the newcomer at first, as long as Max kept his distance. Then there were minor disagreements between the two as Max grew braver and wanted to run and play with his sulky orange lodge mate. But the consensus among Hiawathans was that this behavior would stop when Max was "fixed."

It did not. If anything, their conflict intensified after Max was neutered at six months. Lodge opinion was split between those who thought Max was still acting amorous in spite of being "fixed" and those who saw him as merely kittenish and playful. Whichever it was, Lovey had shifted to a zero tolerance approach, but Max wouldn't leave her alone. Max would follow Lovey around, snarl and pounce in a half-playful, half-aggressive lunge. Lovey would hiss and run; Max would chase. This happened at all hours of the day or night. Not only was the caterwauling disruptive, everyone was concerned that someone would get hurt.

Dale had read a book on cat behavior which suggested that the two combatants would work out their territories if left alone. But the other members of Hiawatha Lodge lacked the patience necessary to play this strategy. The hissing, snarling, and screaming in the middle of the night got on everyone's nerves.

Lovey had years of seniority over Max; and Lovey preferred the upstairs portion of the lodge, coming down primarily to eat and use her litter box. It was determined therefore, that the upstairs belonged to Lovey and the downstairs to Max. All the members of Hiawatha Lodge agreed to this except for Lovey and Max. Lovey ignored her food and litterbox when they were moved upstairs, and Max could not be counted on to stay downstairs. In fact, running up and down the stairs was one of his favorite games.

The open, split-level architecture of the new Hiawatha Lodge did not lend itself to a solid door, but the Hiawathans installed one anyway. The door kept Max downstairs, but Lovey could still get downstairs when she wanted to by jumping from the wide, flat banister. She did this only while everyone except Jan was at work. Jan would stop whatever she was doing, limp after Max the best she could, and lock him in the bathroom for about ten minutes. After Lovey had finished whatever she came down to do, Jan would deposit Lovey on the upstairs side of the door (even though it was a major effort for her to climb the half-flight of steps), and let Max out.

This arrangement held for about 18 months, and might still be working, except that Lovey developed arthritis in her hind quarters. Like Jan, she moved stiffly and appeared in some discomfort. The vet explained that hip replacement surgery would cost $2,000 and might not solve the problem. He recommended periodical Cortisone shots, and said, "Oh, by the way, keep her off of stairs and high places."

The compromise that had worked for a while had to be renegotiated. The best solution Hiawatha Lodge could think of was to reverse the territories. Lovey would get the downstairs and Max the upstairs.

It was a disaster. It took Max less than ten minutes to discover Lovey's route around the door. He obviously had watched her do it. And unlike Lovey, Max did not require a reason to use it. In fact, he was perfectly happy to eat and litter upstairs but he was not content to stay there otherwise. Since he could not return upstairs on his own because of the door, he was almost always downstairs tormenting Lovey. The silver clumps of fur from Max and the tiger fur from Lovey found lying around the downstairs were traumatic for all the Hiawathans, but especially Jan. They held yet another meeting to seek a solution. Their options were poor.

"I could pay for Lovey's operation," said Jan, "but it's a lot of money."

"We could sheetrock the whole thing in," suggested Lois.

"We would have to have Tasks' permission for that," said Dale. "And even if they agreed, there is no way they would ever pay for it."

"We could pay for it ourselves," said Lois.

"That's going to cost more than the hip replacement," said Everett.

"And it would be ugly," said Dale. "The open feel is the whole point of the split level."

The longer they talked about it, the dumber the ideas got. Ed suggested they magnetize Max and Lovey; either both positive or both negative so that they would be magnetically repelled when they tried to attack each other.

"Is that possible?" asked Marsha.

"I don't know."

"Well, like did you see this on TV or something?"

"No, it was just an idea," said Ed as Dale groaned.

No solution ever emerged, at least not one that worked. Eventually, they went with Dale's original strategy of just letting them fight. This was harder on Jan than the others because she was home with Lovey and Max while the others were at work.

Max and Lovey never became friends. They still hiss at each other on occasion. But the other members rarely find patches of fur when they get home from work. And they are not often awakened by angry screams in the middle of the night anymore

anymore either. Somehow, on terms which are not entirely known to the other members, Max and Lovey have come to an understanding.

Next to reorganizing the pantry, the big event in Jan's week now is Di coming over to play cribbage every Saturday evening. The woman Di had the argument with long ago has moved on, but Di has an efficiency apartment downtown and she likes living alone. She had a waitress job for a while but it didn't work out, so she works for Tasks again. She works downtown with the Diamonds and she socializes with some of them, but Jan is her best friend.

They sort of keep track of their cribbage games. Officially Di is ahead 2,117 games to Jan's 1,954, but sometimes when it gets late they forget to record the evening's work in their tally book, and later they argue over whether they did or not. They both agree that Di is ahead, but they disagree by how much.

Occasionally Jan plays cribbage with one of the Hiawathans during the week, but except for Lois, they aren't any good. Some of them will throw Jan a five when its her crib, just out of ignorance.

Di will be sixty-five in a couple of years and plans to retire. Jan is hoping there will be room for Di to return to Hiawatha Lodge for her retirement. Even at full dues, the room and board will cost her less than it costs downtown. But Di says her main goal for retirement is to sleep late every morning. She is not sure how that would work with all the commotion at Hiawatha Lodge. Jan can't figure out how a person can sleep past 7 a.m.

Jan's brother Mike is talking retirement also. He's still farming at seventy-two, but he sold off the dairy herd five years ago and he rents out half the farm to a neighbor. At least at Hiawatha Lodge, Jan has the kitchen to clean and the pantry to keep organized.

Lodge Magic
SCRAPBOOK

30 YEARS C
MEMORIES
– of lodges
– of lodge membe
– of friends

"Work a little, play a little, eat a little, sleep a little — the lodge is a well-rounded life."

"Great house, great job — that's wha the Lodge means to me!"

Deinstitutionalization
begins

1961

Dr. Fairweather
begins work at Palo Alto

1st boo
publish

"Something is always going on."

"I wanted less staff and more independence."

Fairweather Lodge in Arkansas

1968

Lodge Training established at Anoka State Hospital

"Now when I visit my folks, there are things to talk about besides my illness."

"I joined the lodge because I wanted a job but it's so much more."

"A nice house in a nice neighborhood."

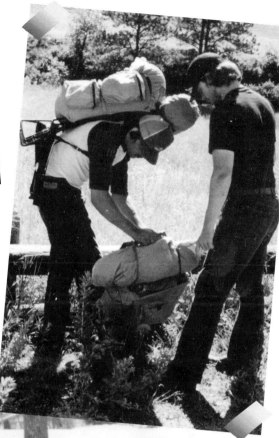

"You always have somebody to do something with."

"I paid my own way when we went to Disney World."

"Going to work is the highlight of my day!"

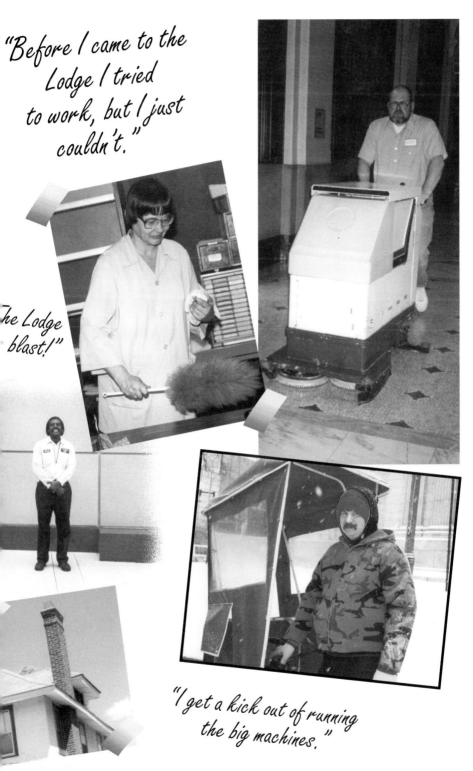

"Before I came to the Lodge I tried to work, but I just couldn't."

he Lodge blast!"

"I get a kick out of running the big machines."

"The most important thing is living
with people who understand my illness"

"You never forget your meds
when you're in a lodge."

1990

"I'm glad to be out of the system and grateful to be in a lodge."

"I've got more confidence now."

Tasks creates remodeling business "Rehab²"

1993

Tasks Unlimited Lodges gets first HOME loan from HUD

"Being in a lodge means never giving up!"

"When I lived alone I didn't eat wel — in the lodge we eat like kings!"

"Good friends make good food taste even better."

"They take my check at the local stores."

"Some people call me a janitor, but I think of myself as an environmental engineer."

Red River floods Grand Forks.
Tasks lodges send relief crews

1998

"The lodge is a win-win proposition!"

"I worked hard to get here, I'm not going to blow it now."

"Tasks has a number of opportunities — you can even become a contract manager."

"Before the lodge I didn't much of a futu — now I do."

1999

First lodge opens in Grand Forks

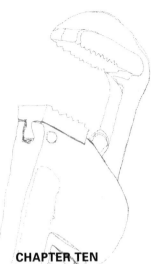

"Why would we call staff?"

Louis Hartwell
Painters Lodge

CHAPTER TEN

PRODIGAL
MECHANIC

The director's phone rang. He picked it up and said, "Hello."

"This is Lou."

"Yeah, Lou."

"Louis Hartwell."

"I know."

"How did you know?"

"I recognized your voice."

"Oh."

"Besides, I don't know that many guys named Lou."

"Oh. They didn't call you or nothing?"

"Who?"

"Uh, the staff here at the hospital."

"Nope. Are you in the hospital?"

There was a slight pause, then Lou said, "Yeah."

"I'm sorry to hear that."

"Well, you know how it goes."

"Yup." The director paused, waiting for Lou to speak. When he did not, the director asked, "What can I do for you, Lou?"

"You remember when I used to be in the Painters Lodge?"

"Of course I do."

"And I did pretty well there for a while, right?"

"You did great."

"Well, ... do you think I could come back? If the Painters are full I would settle for any lodge."

"I don't see why not. And I think the front bedroom at the Painters is empty."

"You mean it?"

"Well, you were the best mechanic they ever had, and I happen to know they are having trouble with their van ..."

"They're still having trouble with the transmission on the Suburban?"

"No, we replaced that with a brand new Ford Club a couple years ago, but they've had to replace the water pump or the fuel pump, or something, three times already."

"And the dealership doesn't know what's wrong?'

"I guess not. Anyway, I assume the Painters would be happy to have you back."

"Wow, that's a relief. You're going to have to talk to the hospital staff here about it though. They don't want to let me out. Hold on a minute and I'll go get one."

"Wait a minute. Lou?"

"Yeah?"

"What hospital are you in?"

"Mendota State Hospital."

"Uff da ... Lou, you still there?"

"Yeah."

"What ward are you in?"

"Youngdahl."

"Is that still the security unit?"

"Yeah."

"Lou?"

"Yeah."

"You aren't in restraints, are you?"

"Not for over a week now."

"This is Nurse Wilson. Whom am I speaking to?"

"This is the director of Tasks Unlimited."

"What can I do for you?"

"Well, I was just speaking to Lou there, apparently he's one of your patients. He's expressing interest in coming to a lodge."

"I don't see how that would be possible."

"Why is that?"

"Isn't the lodge that program where people live in a small group without supervision? And they all hold down jobs?"

"That's us."

"There is no way Mr. Hartwell could ever function at that level. We've had much higher functioning patients than him turned down by your training program."

"Actually, I was thinking that if the Painters Lodge wants him, we might skip the training program entirely, put him directly into the lodge."

"Why would you even consider that when we have higher functioning patients you won't take?"

"I guess I don't know the other cases you refer to, but Lou sounded pretty good on the phone."

"On the phone?"

"His voice was real clear."

"His voice?"

"Well, I've known him for years. He seemed nervous but he didn't seem agitated."

"I'm sure the judge handling Mr. Hartwell's case will be impressed with your diagnostic skills."

"You're telling me he's committed?"

"He certainly is."

"For how long?"

"Indefinitely, with an annual review."

"When does his first review come up?"

"Last year, I suppose. He just had his second review last month."

"He's not M.I. and D, is he?"

"Correct; he's been certified as mentally ill and dangerous."

"Anyone seriously hurt?"

"Several."

"How many?"

"On the streets before his commitment, or since he got here?"

"You're not telling me he has continued to assault people since he was committed to the hospital and you got him on meds?"

"He certainly has."

"How many?"

"People injured? Or separate incidents of assault?"

"Never mind ... Nurse Williams?"

"Wilson."

"Wilson, I'm sorry. Can you tell me what meds he is on now?"

"I don't have his chart handy, but I couldn't give you that information without a release anyway. I've said more than I should already. He's been on everything once or twice."

"Can you tell me when his last med change was?"

"Probably a couple of weeks ago."

"Has he assaulted anyone in the past two weeks."

"No."

"Would you do me a favor?"

"What is it?"

"I'm going to fax you a release form. Would you ask Lou to sign it? And after he does, would you look up his current meds and tell me what he's on when I call back this afternoon?"

"Your Honor, I believe Mr. Hartwell is an excellent candidate for a provisional discharge to the Painters Lodge."

"Painters Lodge? Never heard of it."

"It's part of the Tasks Unlimited system, Your Honor."

"Those aren't entirely secure facilities, are they?"

"No sir, there would be virtually no security."

"How can you even suggest exposing the community to that sort of risk? Are you familiar with this patient's history?"

"Yes, Your Honor, I am very familiar with Mr. Hartwell's history, and that's why I propose the Painters Lodge."

"Explain."

"Your Honor, Mr. Hartwell was previously committed to Mendota State Hospital from July of 1976 to July, 1980. In those days, there was a Fairweather Lodge Training Unit on the Mendota campus. Mr. Hartwell was referred to the Fairweather Unit in September of 1979. Although he struggled initially, he achieved enough progress that his commitment was dropped the following summer and he was admitted to the Painters Lodge in October of 1980.

"Mr. Hartwell did quite well in the interdependent milieu of the Painters Lodge. He was initially elected Lodge Chairman in February of 1982, and subsequently achieved the status of permanent-chair-until-recall, as no one was ever sufficiently dissatisfied to run against him. He also held a steady, full time job with what was then Tasks Unlimited Janitorial Services. He was promoted to Crew Chief with partial responsibility for supervising four other workers, and finally to Contract Manager, responsible for all contract cleaning at the Gemco Building. He managed a $150,000 account and supervised twelve men."

"How many of them did he assault?"

"No one, Your Honor, nor anyone else during the period 1980 to 1986."

"And then he became a one-man crime wave?"

"Well, sort of. May I continue?"

"Go on."

"During this period of successful adjustment, Mr. Hartwell was taking 200mg of injectable Prolixin every two weeks. This was a rather high dosage of a now obsolete medication, but shortly before his discharge in 1980, the doctor at Mendota had determined this to be Mr. Hartwell's ideal dosage. Our psychiatrist, Dr. Robert Hanson, maintained this dosage. During the early eighties, Dr. Hanson tried several other medications to control the Parkinsonian side-effects of the Prolixin, unfortunately to no avail.

"By 1986, Mr. Hartwell had developed obvious symptoms of Tardive Dyskinesia, a malady often associated with long-term, high-dose use of Prolixin. The most problematic of the symptoms was a rather severe twisting of the right side of Mr. Hartwell's face, which occurred approximately every four to five seconds. Slightly less often while sleeping, slightly more often when he was nervous.

"Mr. Hartwell requested relief from these most unpleasant side effects. Although we were sympathetic to his concerns about the tic, my staff opposed any changes, because we felt Mr. Hartwell's mental health was more important than his appearance. We especially opposed conversion from injectable Prolixin every two weeks to daily oral administration. Although there is an equivalent oral dose, we considered the risk of deception and noncompliance, given his history, to be unacceptable.

"For a while, the staff position prevailed with Dr. Hanson. Unfortunately, however, there have been numerous lawsuits in which doctors were held liable for causing a patient's Tardive Dyskinesia by prescribing suspect medications such as Prolixin. Ultimately, Dr. Hanson found his liability risks to weigh more than our conservative counsel. Already by mid-1986, there were several medications not available in 1980 which promised therapeutic results equivalent to Prolixin, with fewer side effects.

"So ultimately it was agreed that Mr. Hartwell would be taken off the Prolixin and tried on some of these newer meds. We suggested a prophylactic hospitalization during the experimentation, but Mr. Hartwell understandably felt this was unnecessary, as he had exhibited virtually no symptoms of psychosis during the previous five years. A compromise was reached through which he signed a contract agreeing to voluntary hospitalization if and when we observed any signs of a developing thought disorder. And just to be safe, we rearranged our staffing pattern to double our observation opportunities.

"But it didn't work. Approximately five weeks from the date of his last Prolixin injection, and despite administration of the best drugs available in 1986, Mr. Hartwell began to decompensate. The first incident occurred at work, where he loudly and abusively berated one of his subordinates for improper technique in mopping a floor. This was overheard by other crew members and quickly reported to staff. The details of the situation were ambiguous, however, and Mr. Hartwell calmly defended his behavior as misunderstood. We chose not to invoke the hospitalization contract, but we doubled the observation yet again.

"Two nights later, the Painters Lodge sat down after work to a steak dinner. Everyone, including the evening's cook, agrees that the steaks were overdone, but most felt they were still edible. Mr. Hartwell announced that his was not edible, and threw it away uneaten. He further insisted that none of the steaks were edible, and threw them all in the garbage, even though this meant grabbing them off of other people's plates against their objections. He went on to accuse the cook of having burned the steaks on purpose. He had some cocka-mamie theory no one quite remembers now, but it was generally agreed at the time to be paranoia.

"Staff responded immediately to the emergency phone call. We invoked the contract provisions calling for voluntary hospi-talization. Mr. Hartwell again described his behavior as misun-derstood and denied the existence of the contract. When a copy of the contract was produced, he insisted it was invalid on the grounds he had been tricked into signing it. He went on to insist that the steaks had been burnt as a pretext to invoke the contract. Over the next thirty-six hours, he continued adamant-ly to refuse voluntary hospitalization, or even to see Dr. Hanson for an evaluation. I discussed this with Mr. Hartwell in person, but to no avail.

"As obvious as his decompensation was to us, we all agreed we were not even close to meeting the standards for involuntary hospitalization. He was not suicidal. He had not hit anyone. He had not even threatened anyone, not for more than six years. Dr. Hanson's hands were tied. He ordered the emergency administration of injectable Prolixin, but only if Mr. Hartwell would appear at his office to receive it. Hartwell would not.

"By this time, the members of Painters Lodge were clearly frightened of Mr. Hartwell. They understood, better than staff perhaps, his need for hospitalization. But if hospitalization was off the table, they wanted him out. It was not necessary for the Painters to formally expel him as the feelings were mutual. Mr. Hartwell was disgusted with their ingratitude, and accused two members of plotting against him all along. He left the Painters Lodge and the Tasks Program. There was nothing we could legally do to stop him. He left no forwarding address. A few weeks later we got a tip where he was living and we sent our social worker to talk to him. But he wouldn't open the door, and screamed at her to leave him alone.

"Your Honor, I am not familiar with the details of Mr. Hartwell's life over the following twenty months. I believe you have in front of you the records of multiple arrests for assault beginning in March of 1987, which led to Mr. Hartwell's commitment to Mendota State Hospital as M.I. and D.

"But I wish to call your attention to the seven incidents of assault, alleged assault, or near assault committed between June of 1988 and May of this year, while he was under the care of Mendota State Hospital. The Mendota records show, coincidentally, that he was given seven different medications, and dozens of different dosages and combinations thereof, during this period, none of which allowed Mr. Hartwell to achieve the level of functioning he enjoyed during his six years at the Painters Lodge.

"On July 5, 1990, however, Mr. Hartwell was given an injection of 200mg of Prolixin. These injections have been repeated every two weeks since then. I suggest to you that the man who stands before you today, the man who called me on July 21 of this year, is the same man who was the Chairman of the Painters Lodge and the Janitorial Services Contract Manager at Gemco from 1981 to 1986. More important, this is not the same man who assaulted all those people between 1986 and this past May."

"If it wasn't Louis Hartwell, who was it?"

"Your Honor, the Lou Hartwell who takes 200mg of injectable Prolixin every two weeks is not the same person as the Lou Hartwell who doesn't."

"And what about this Tardive Dyskinesia problem? Have

you solved that?"

"No, your Honor, we have not. He doesn't show any signs of it yet, but it's really too early to tell. There is one promising side-effect medication which was not available four years ago, but who knows?"

"So your doctor has a better lawyer now?"

"I'm not sure about that, Your Honor, but Dr. Hanson has agreed, if Mr. Hartwell is released to his care, to maintain him on injectable Prolixin, at least until the Tardive Dyskinesia returns."

"And then what?"

"We're not sure. Obviously our counsel will be prophylactic hospitalization should it become desirable to experiment with other medications."

"Why take the risk at all?"

"Quite frankly, Your Honor, nobody takes Prolixin anymore, specifically because of the nasty side effects. Our local pharmacy doesn't even stock it; we'll have to special order it.

"There are new drugs available every day. There is a promising new drug called Clozaril due on the market soon. Mr. Hartwell was approved for field testing of Clozaril earlier in his current stay at Mendota, but unfortunately he was randomly assigned to the control group where he received Haldol instead."

"And you think this Clozaril, whatever, will work as well as the Prolixin?"

"I have no idea, Your Honor. However, by this time next year there will be something else, and the year after that, something new again. But my recommendation is that you make 200mg of Prolixin every two weeks a condition of his provisional discharge to the Painters Lodge."

"I'm a judge. I'm not a physician. And neither are you. No matter how convinced you are that 200mg of Prolixin is the magic bullet here, and even if I'm persuaded that you are correct, I can't order a specific prescription."

"Your Honor, the 200mg of Prolixin has already been prescribed. You could stipulate in your order that any change in medications would require automatic re-hospitalization."

"Maybe we should keep him locked up until they find something that works."

"Prolixin does work, Your Honor. It could be a long time until a better alternative comes along. In the meantime, he doesn't need to be locked up. He was a productive citizen when he was at the Painters Lodge the first time, and he could be again."

"And then he stops taking the Prolixin for whatever reason, and he becomes a threat to the community again. Six, eight, ten years from now we're all right here having this same conversation all over again."

"It's possible, Your Honor, but you can't keep him locked up forever."

"Well, you're right about that." After a long sigh, "I guess we'll give this lodge plan a try. But if Mr. Hartwell gives me reason to regret it, you will too."

While Lou was assaulting people at Mendota State Hospital, the timer motor on the washing machine at the Painters Lodge burned out. The machine wouldn't run. Alan, the Lodge Chairman, called a meeting to discuss the situation. The initial consensus was to buy a new machine. But Trevor, the Lodge Treasurer, reminded the group that their finances were tight at the moment for two reasons: 1) they had built their current budget on the assumption of a full, six-man lodge, but Harvey had married Sandi and moved out and nobody ever replaced him, so only five guys were paying dues; and 2) the Painters had decided, over Trevor's objection, to continue purchasing the deluxe cable package with HBO.

Thus admonished, the Painters' discussion turned to purchasing a used machine versus calling a repair man, and the probability of getting ripped off either way.

Reluctantly, the usually reserved Calvin spoke up, "It's probably the timer motor. If it is, we could probably pick one up at the junk yard for under $10. I think I could replace it."

Some of the Painters were privately skeptical that Calvin, who was unable to keep their two-year-old van running, was much of a mechanic, but it was unanimously agreed to try his plan. It worked.

There was one problem with Calvin's repair. He inadvertently disabled the automatic shut-off on the fill cycle. This meant that one needed to stand there and watch the machine fill up, and then switch it to "agitate" when there seemed to be enough water. Everything else worked fine. Considering that the entire project had cost the Painters only $8, this was considered a very minor inconvenience, and Calvin was roundly congratulated.

About six months later, Lou returned to the Painters Lodge, filling the lone vacancy. Calvin, the cook who had overgrilled the steaks, had vivid memories of the incident and was still nervous about Lou. Everyone else was glad to have him back.

By Painters tradition, the Treasurer's job included the responsibility of orienting new members. But Trevor questioned if it was really necessary. "Lou," Trevor observed, "knows the drill."

"Fair enough," said Chairman Alan. "Just give him a current copy of the lodge rules, and tell him to see me if he has any questions."

Lou was not inclined to ask many questions.

The other Painters worked half-time and collected Social Security, but Lou immediately resumed working full time. His third day back at the Painters Lodge, Lou noticed he was getting low on clean shirts. He had intended to wash and dry a load before going to work, but he overslept a little and just barely had time to throw things in the washer before catching the bus to work. Ordinarily, the other Painters would have been around the lodge for a while. But as luck would have it, that was a bowling day, and the others were headed out the back door to the van as Lou went out the front door.

The overflow drain in the laundry room absorbed some of the runoff, but not enough to keep up. By the time the Painters returned from work, a half an inch of water covered the basement floor. As soon as the problem was discovered, the entire lodge convened on the basement steps to ponder the disaster. It didn't take long to figure out what had happened. Nothing much was damaged, except for an old rug.

"Well, have a good time cleaning it up, boys," said Larry. "It's my night to make dinner. I'll call you when it's ready."

As professional janitors, the Painters were better equipped than most households to clean it up. They owned two mop buckets and three rag mops. Alan handed one each to Trevor, Calvin, and Lou. Calvin and Trevor both gave Alan puzzled looks, but it was Lou who spoke first.

"I ain't mopping that up!"

"Yeah," said Calvin and Trevor, "Why us?"

Alan explained his reasoning, "Lou, you left the water running."

"I've been working all day while you FREELOADERS were bowling. And what kind of a moron disables the automatic shutoff when replacing a timer motor?" Lou asked glaring at Calvin.

"Nevertheless," said Alan. "And Calvin, you're the one that screwed the washer up."

"I didn't see you trying to fix it," said Calvin.

"Nevertheless," said Alan. "And Trevor, you are doubly guilty: once for encouraging the lodge to go cheap on the repair, and second for ducking your responsibilities as Treasurer."

"You agreed," protested Trevor.

"Nevertheless," said Alan.

Lou was quick to point out Alan's complicity in both decisions, as well as his general lack of leadership, "In the old days, a lodge chairman knew what was going on."

The argument continued, but they mopped as they argued. Trevor suggested Alan be the one to dump the buckets in the washtub. Alan initially agreed, but then realized that keeping two buckets empty was more work than mopping. In the end, the four of them rotated through the three mops and the bucket detail, arguing culpability all the time.

They mopped and argued for an hour. They argued all through dinner. They mopped and argued for another hour. Phil sat on the basement steps and watched. He mopped a little now and then when the others were tired, but mostly he watched and offered unsolicited advice. When Larry was finished with the dishes he joined Phil on the steps. It was better than TV.

It just so happened that the director of Tasks Unlimited was on tour that evening with a new board member. He had warned the Painters he would probably drop by, but in the excitement they forgot all about him. The director knocked on the front door, but they couldn't hear him over the fans they had set up to dry the floor. They walked around to the back to see if the Painters' van was there, and seeing it was, knocked on the back door. Larry let the director and the new board member in, and explained what had happened.

The standing water was gone. They were just finishing a few wet spots, but a long way from finishing the argument. On the way over, the director had been explaining the vital role of the Lodge Coordinator to the new board member. He asked if they had called their Coordinator to tell him about the disaster.

"Why would we call staff?" asked Lou. "We only got three mops."

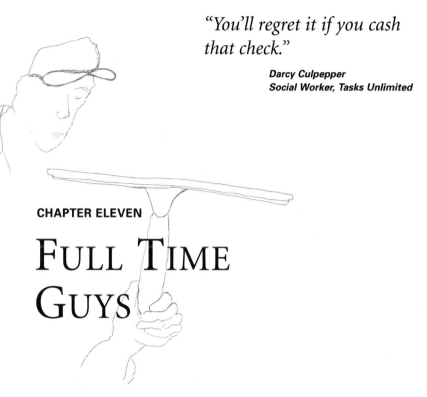

"You'll regret it if you cash that check."

Darcy Culpepper
Social Worker, Tasks Unlimited

CHAPTER ELEVEN

FULL TIME
GUYS

A group of people from another state visited Tasks Unlimited to learn about the lodge program. The director was showing them around. The tour included an office building where lodge members were employed as janitors. The visitors were huddled around the director in the janitorial office. At the same time, Lou was inventorying supplies at the other end of the room. As usual, he was talking to himself as he worked.

"FREELOADERS!" Lou was overheard to say. "Bunch of FREELOADERS sitting around the lodge when they should be working." When he noticed the tour group looking at him he lowered his voice. He continued speaking but his words were now inaudible except for the repeated term, "FREELOADERS!" in an agitated tone. The director was embarrassed, and moved his guests out of the room on the pretext of inspecting the cafeteria. The next time he saw Lou, he asked him what he had been upset about. Lou denied he had been upset. He didn't seem to remember the incident.

"Something about freeloaders," the director said. "You kept talking about freeloaders."

"That's what I call 'em," said Lou.

"Call who?"

"The rest of my lodge, that's who. All they do is sit around all day when they should be working."

"I've heard they work pretty hard," said the director.

"For four hours," (Lou worked eight hours a day) "you call that working?"

"Sure I do. You've got to remember they're disabled."

"FREELOADERS! The whole world is full of FREELOAD-ERS. In the old days, lodge members knew how to work."

"Come off it, Lou. Lodge members work just as hard as they ever did. There were always some drawing Social Security Disability."

"Not as many," insisted Lou. "It wasn't so easy to get disability in the old days."

The director knew Lou loved playing the curmudgeon, but the question stuck in the back of his mind. A couple of days later he reviewed the records. Lou had a point. Lou and several other old-time lodge members had been denied disability during the 70's, despite their significant illness. If they wanted to stay in the lodge, they had little choice but to work full time. They had been working full time ever since. But something had changed in the mid-80's, and for the past several years, almost everyone entering the lodge system was on disability. Talking to his staff and the lodge members about it, the director learned that collecting disability, and protecting one's eligibility for disability, had become a fundamental component of the lodge culture. Anyone working full time would lose their disability, so no one ever did.

"This isn't what Dr. Fairweather had in mind," thought the director. "Lodges are supposed to be about self sufficiency, and first-class citizenship, not about maintaining eligibility for government handouts."

The director called a staff meeting and announced to a stunned group of Lodge Coordinators and other staff that things were going to change. "From now on, encouraging lodge members to maximize their earning potential is going to be a top priority at Tasks. If that means people lose their eligibility for disability, then Tasks needs to make certain they earn enough not to need disability. We cannot allow their illness to prevent them from earning a living wage," he proclaimed.

"Brave talk, but complete nonsense," thought most of the Lodge Coordinators. They looked to Darcy, Tasks' social worker for help in explaining to the director why it was impossible for people with serious illnesses like schizophrenia to work full time.

But Darcy had a funny smile on her face. She knew the Director was full of goofy ideas. Most of his proclamations were just trial balloons; if she ignored them long enough, they would drift away. But she wasn't going to ignore this idea. Darcy was the only person in the room who actually liked the idea. "The director doesn't know it," she thought, "but this is the best idea he ever had."

Darcy thought to herself how difficult it was going to be to sell the idea. People with mental illness often do not perceive themselves as mentally ill, which is one of the reasons they tend not to take their medications as prescribed. In order that they might have a chance of successful treatment, somebody has to tell them. Usually, no one sets out to convince them that their situation is hopeless and they will never be able to live like other people; they assume it. In doing so they become special people, to whom the normal rules do not apply.

Take work, for example. As special people, they are encouraged to feel good about themselves, but are systematically denied any opportunity to work, which happens to be the primary source of self esteem in our society. Besides self esteem, work also produces income, which is helpful in paying rent and buying groceries. In the tradition of the New Deal, rent and groceries for people with mental illness have become a government responsibility. Two federal programs, Supplemental Security Income (SSI) and Social Security Disability Insurance (SSDI) were created for this purpose. The details of the two programs differ, but the basic contract is the same. If people can prove they are disabled, and avoid earning any income, the government will provide them with enough income to stay alive. Just barely.

In the past, some people were "handicapped." This meant the same thing as it does in bowling or golf. Some people are not quite as skilled as others, so you have to spot them a few pins or a few strokes to make things fair. Somehow, the term "handicapped" became politically incorrect. Nowadays, the correct term is "disabled" which, taken literally, means incapable. SSI and SSDI demand a standard of 100% disability for mental illness. (A person with a back injury can be considered 30% disabled, or 70% disabled, and receive adjusted benefits while still working, but a person with mental illness has to prove 100% disability, i.e., complete and total uselessness.) And proving one's self totally useless is not as much fun as it sounds.

Social Security has created a classic Catch 22 setup, closely analogous to that described by Heller in his famous novel. A person who really was totally disabled would be incapable of filling the forms out correctly and turning them in on time, which, of course, is a fundamental requirement for any government program. (People who can complete government forms without assistance are not only employable, they are management material.) Successful completion of an SSI/SSDI application generally requires a team of parents, siblings, social workers and case managers. And of course the application is generally denied, requiring an appeal. Not only does an incapable person have no chance of acquiring disability status through his or her own efforts, even a person with a mediocre support team is unlikely to succeed. Achieving certification of disability on the grounds of mental illness requires a determined effort by several highly able people.

Generally, one of the team members, exhausted and frustrated by this epic struggle with a giant bureaucracy, will complain to the beneficiary of these efforts. "This is very hard. If and when we finally win and get you certified as disabled, don't ever, ever do anything to screw it up. Don't you dare, for example, ever earn money. If someone offers you a job, run away as fast as you can."

In addition to this advice being repeated over and over until it becomes the Eleventh Commandment in the subject's mind, the subject may even have to testify at the appeal hearing. The successful applicant/witness will have been coached in advance. "Whatever the judge asks you, remember to say that you are completely and totally incapable of any kind of employment, now and forever."

Such is the requirement for getting enough government support to actually survive.

In spite of all this, SSI/SSDI recipients are allowed to work a little without losing their eligibility, as long as they don't make any real money. In fact, the lodge system was built on the fiscal model of everyone working a little. Tasks staff knew the SSI and SSDI rules and helped lodge members understand how much they could afford to work.

Even that was sometimes a tough sell. Since total inability is a reasonable interpretation of the term "100% disabled," new admissions to Tasks had to first be convinced that they were indeed capable of performing productive work. Secondly, they needed to be convinced that their parents, their social worker, and everyone else who had warned them, never work, were wrong; that despite the warnings and the apparent contradiction of terms, they could actually work part-time while collecting disability benefits.

Both persuasions were often difficult. The latter was made even more challenging by the complexity of the SSI/SSDI rules. (Think of the instructions for calculating depreciation on an income tax return, and then double the obtuseness.) Well-meaning parents and social workers, who did not understand the SSI/SSDI rules as well as Tasks, shook their heads and said, "I'm not so sure. It looks risky to me." A phone call or written exchange with the local Social Security office did not always help either, since not all Social Security personnel understood the Social Security rules. If the inquisitive parent or social worker got the wrong person on the phone, they might have their fears confirmed: following Tasks' advice might cost their son or client his disability.

The growth of the lodge program, however, proved the battle over part-time employment could be won. Lodge members had become comfortable with the idea that working twenty hours per week and collecting SSI/SSDI was the natural order of things. They were proud of themselves for working half-time because they knew that most people with mental illness just lie around all day, depending entirely on SSI/SSDI. Lodge members, although collecting SSI/SSDI, nevertheless considered themselves working men and women, and they held their heads up high when they went in to cash their paychecks.

And yet, because they had been certified as disabled, they also depended on the government checks. The Lodge Coordinators and I had kept track of the SSI/SSDI rules so that no one accidentally lost their disability. In some ways, lodge members had become enslaved by the mental health system and SSI/SSDI. They performed janitorial work for twenty hours each week, and there was ample evidence that they were good at it. But somehow they continued to believe they were incapable of supporting themselves.

Darcy held a meeting. She made up flyers and sent them to all the lodges, "Come to a meeting at Tasks and learn about opportunities to work full time." She didn't know how many would attend. Talking with other staff, most of whom thought that she and the director were irresponsible in suggesting full time work for lodge members, she feared that perhaps no one would attend. She bought snacks for eight people.

Thirty-five lodge residents, sixty percent of the Tasks lodge population at that time, showed up. They were cautious in their enthusiasm, but they were curious. "What exactly did she have in mind? Could they work full time without losing their disability?"

"No," she told them. I am talking real work for real money. Far too much to retain eligibility for government handouts."

The objections surfaced immediately.

"I have schizophrenia," said Chuckie.

"I take a lot of meds," said Dale.

"My mother told me not to," said Chris.

"I have bad knees," said Judy.

Darcy did the best she could to counter these and numerous other lame excuses. The biggest question, which she could not answer broadly because each individual situation varied, was, "Will I come out ahead or behind?" She promised to meet with everyone to review their personal finances. She passed around a piece of paper to sign if they were interested. "No obligation," she assured them. "This is just exploratory." She was pleased to see fourteen people sign up.

Her optimism turned to pessimism, however, when she started meeting with each individual. When she calculated the additional income they could earn, minus taxes, and compared it to the tax-free disability they would be giving up, it was generally a push. Those who earned the highest hourly rates, or received the smallest SSI/SSDI checks to start with, came out slightly ahead. Those who earned the lowest hourly rates, or received the biggest SSI/SSDI checks, or who were receiving some sort of free services based on their low income, came out slightly behind.

Mostly they came out even. "If you work eight hours every day instead of four hours, you will come out 85 cents per day ahead," she explained to Dale.

Four of the fourteen looked at the math and said, "No way."

Most of the fourteen looked at the math, scratched their heads, and looked at Darcy. They expected an explanation of why they should attempt something so illogical. She had no explanation to give them. She was struggling to explain it to herself.

Among the fourteen, Darcy considered Silas the least likely candidate for full time work. She had heard others complain about what a poor worker he was, and she suspected that the minimum wage, which Tasks paid him, was more than he was worth. And she knew from her own experience that he was emotionally needy, dependent on staff for constant reassurance. Working full time would give him even less access to staff, whereas he seemed to need more. She reviewed his finances with him only out of courtesy.

When she did the calculation, Silas lost $36 per month by converting to full time.

"I'll do it," said Silas.

"I don't think you understand," Darcy explained, "This is $36 less."

"Okay," said Silas.

"Okay you understand?"

"Okay I'll do it."

"What I'm trying to show you here is that if you work twice as hard, you will end up with less money."

"Only $36 less."

"Right, $36 LESS!"

"I'll do it."

"Silas, are you sure you understand me?"

"Don't you want me to work full time?"

Darcy had to stop and think. A month ago when she heard the director's speech, she thought it was a terrific idea. But after two weeks of individual calculations she wasn't certain. The best cases came out only slightly ahead. Silas was coming out behind. It didn't make much sense. "Why do you want to work full time when it will cost you money?"

"It would be nice to get off welfare, to pay my own way for a change." Silas held his head up real straight when he said this, and he looked her right in the eye. Darcy suddenly remembered why she had thought it was a good idea.

In the days that followed, she pondered Silas' predicament. She also thought about the other thirteen, "It is curious that only four have dismissed the idea outright. Despite overwhelming evidence that working full time would provide almost no financial gain, nine have not actually committed themselves one way or the other. It's as if they were waiting for me to give them a reason to ignore the laws of economics."

It so happened that Tasks had just acquired a new home which it was frantically converting into a lodge to relieve overcrowding in existing lodges. Due to fortunate coincidence, this was a beautiful house in an upscale neighborhood. It would clearly be the nicest lodge Tasks had owned up to that time.

That gave Darcy an idea. She went to the director and asked, "Who gets the new lodge?"

"Any moves will be voluntary, of course," he said. "I expect we'll get more than six volunteers, so we'll have to choose somehow. Mostly seniority, I guess, with priority to volunteers from the most overcrowded lodges."

"I have a better idea," said Darcy. "Let's make full time employment a condition for the new lodge."

The director balked at first. It wasn't Fairweather-like for Tasks to make rules for lodges. But Darcy convinced him it was no more arbitrary than seniority or the standard lodge admission requirements which Tasks controlled. "And it's just a start-up standard," she argued. "Once the lodge exists, the members can adopt or repeal the rule as they choose." Her most convincing argument was when she reminded the director that encouraging full time work had been his idea in the first place.

When it was announced that the six slots in the beautiful new lodge were reserved for full-timers, ten signed up; five Darcy was expecting, including Silas, and five she hadn't expected. Two of the latter had not even attended the first full time meeting.

The director let Darcy select the lucky six. Silas was her first choice. She knew he was a long-shot to succeed, but she felt that he, as her inspiration to proceed, deserved the opportunity. She also picked Carl from Bay Lodge, whose constant efforts to buy and sell cars was like a second job already. Then Alan from the Painters, who was better off working than in bed. Then Phil, also of the Painters, who was anxious to prove his worth to society. Then Dean from the Spirits, who was as strong as a horse. And finally Warren from Bay Lodge, who received so little Social Security that he didn't have much to lose.

The Diamond Lodge, as they named themselves, all succeeded.

Janitorial work involves strenuous physical labor, and they weren't accustomed to eight hours of it, so the first couple of weeks were incredibly tiring. The second night, Warren was supposed to cook dinner, but he insisted he was too tired. So they had to order pizza, further straining their already strained budget. The next night, Silas started cooking as soon as they got home at 9:45, but by the time he got dinner on the table, maybe 10:30, Warren and Alan had gone to bed and wouldn't get up to eat. And getting anything done on the weekend was hopeless; everybody slept all weekend.

By the end of the second month, however, their stamina had increased dramatically. Darcy had told them it would, but they had been skeptical. The Diamonds were able to clean the house, buy groceries, fix meals, mow the lawn, hold group meetings to discuss lodge management, generally everything the other lodges were doing, while working twice as many hours.

Initially, they agreed to forego participation in the Tasks' recreation program. Some of the mid-day activities conflicted directly with their work schedule, and they had set Saturdays aside to do chores around the lodge. Gradually, however, they began to miss the recreational portion of the program. Dean missed the softball and bowling; Warren missed the cultural activities, like plays and museums; and Silas missed the social aspects, just sitting around drinking coffee with the female members of the other lodges, for example. Everyone felt a sense of loss at being cut off from Tasks-sponsored recreation.

As the months crept by, they slowly figured out ways to

reconnect. Chores could get done on Sunday (after church by those who went to church), and those with family obligations on Sunday could squeeze more into the weeks if they put their minds to it.

As the annual bowling tournament, a one-morning-a-week-for-six-weeks event, approached, they couldn't help but think about the fact that Dean and Carl were among the top bowlers in all the lodges. And Alan and Warren were at least average bowlers. If they could figure out how to participate, they were obvious favorites to capture the title. All they had to do was get up a half hour earlier and start work an hour later on bowling days. This meant they had to work an hour later that night, so bowling days were long days; but it wasn't that bad.

Even Darcy was surprised when their energy level continued to grow. By the end of the first year, they found they had more energy after working eight hours than they had previously had after working four. On weekends they were dynamos — gardening, shopping, working on old cars. Alan signed up for a GED program he had been putting off for years. Dean took up tennis again.

Silas' mom was astonished at his energy. She jumped to the conclusion that Tasks had lowered his meds to allow him to work full time. Silas explained that this was not the case. His sleeping medication had been discontinued because he no longer needed it (he was physically exhausted by the end of his shift), but Dr. Bob had not changed his Haldol since the Lodge Training Program.

One problem which neither Darcy nor any of the Diamonds had anticipated was the reluctance of Social Security to accept their new-found independence. Phil and Silas were on SSI, where their checks fluctuated every month; SSI quickly caught on that they were earning significantly more and the SSI stopped coming.

SSDI was a different matter.

SSDI used a fixed number ($500 per month in those days) to define "Substantial Gainful Activity." SSDI recipients were allowed to earn up to that amount without any effect on their checks. But if they crossed the line, even once, they were goners. They were no longer considered disabled, and their checks would stop forever. It was the disaster lodge residents had lived in fear of for many years.

Having now changed their outlook on life, the Diamonds attempted to take the bull by the horns. Darcy drafted a letter to SSDI which Alan, Carl, Dean, and Warren all copied and signed. Alan's read:

Dear Social Security Disability Insurance:

I am no longer disabled. I have recently accepted a job which pays far more than your definition of Substantial Gainful Activity, so I am no longer eligible for SSDI. I still have mental difficulties from time to time, and I was truly disabled in the past. I appreciate the financial support I received from your office over the years, but I no longer need it.

Yours Truly,

Alan Kovac

Diamond Lodge

The Diamonds were excited about the letters and they wanted to mail them right away, but Darcy made them wait until the end of the first month. Privately, she wasn't certain they would all last a month. All four did, and they all signed and mailed the letters with tremendous pride.

Darcy explained that it would take the SSDI office a couple of months to catch up with them. In the meantime, the Diamonds might continue to receive monthly SSDI checks. "Do not spend them," she warned. "Better yet, don't even cash them.

The smart thing to do is send them back."

They tried this, but it did not work.

Within weeks, SSDI would send the original check, or sometimes a reissued check, back to the Diamond who had returned it. Alan's re-returned check was accompanied by a letter insisting that it was no mistake, the money was definitely his.

"I told you it would take a while," Darcy warned. "But do not think of this as your money regardless of what the letter from SSDI says. They will eventually figure it out, and then they are going to want their money back. If you spend it, you're going to be in trouble."

And SSDI did catch on to Warren relatively soon. Approximately three months after Warren sent SSDI the letter renouncing eligibility, SSDI sent him a letter announcing their decision that he was no longer eligible. The letter went on to explain his right to appeal the decision. Much to Warren's consternation, however, they demanded return of the past three checks, which he had already returned.

"Plan B," Darcy advised Alan, Carl and Dean, is to keep all your SSDI checks, unendorsed, in the lodge cash box. When you finally get your termination notice, you can send them all back." She expected the other three termination notices would arrive soon, but the next to receive a notice was Carl, eight months later.

On the twelve-month anniversary of sending their "I am no longer eligible" letter, Alan and Dean were still getting checks. The cash box was getting full. Alan was struggling financially and Dean had always wanted a motorcycle. The checks in the cash box totaled several thousand dollars each.

"Please don't cash them," Darcy pleaded, "You'll be sorry if you do."

Three weeks later, Alan got his termination notice demanding, under threat of criminal prosecution, the return of all the money. He and Darcy sent the checks by registered mail. One week later, Dean received his thirteenth check. It was sixteen months before Dean received his termination, and his letter did not request the return of the checks. "It might take five years, but they'll come after you," advised Darcy, standing over Dean's shoulder as he sent the checks back.

As the Diamond Lodge resumed showing up for social functions, the other lodges were dismayed to learn that the Diamonds had developed a "tude," a certain smug and condescending attitude that the other lodges did not care for. But the resentment the other lodges felt was tinged with envy.

Initially, people started wishing they were Diamonds. Those who had formally applied but not been chosen blamed Darcy. Those who had been casually interested, but had not formally applied, still blamed Darcy; she should have been more persistent in persuading them. Those who had not shown any interest at all were miffed anyway; "If only I had known," they said. For a while, some held the secret belief that one of the Diamonds, perhaps Silas, would not make it. This would create an opening which several people saw themselves filling.

Once it became clear that the Diamonds, even Silas, were flourishing, other plots emerged. Tasks was still acquiring property and starting approximately one new lodge per year. Why not a second full time lodge?

Denny at the Flagstone Lodge had a better idea. Three of the Flags had recently expressed interest in full time work, and there wasn't any obvious reason the other two couldn't. Why not just turn the existing Flagstone Lodge into a full time lodge?

The Flag's Lodge Coordinator was skeptical; she thought it would not be fair to the Flags' senior member, Victor. Victor was sixty-one and had been a Flag for over twenty years. It didn't seem fair to place those kinds of demands on him.

"No problem. I'm not the one who stays up late watching TV every night and then can't get up the next morning. I can keep up with these whippersnappers," said Victor, referring to Denny and other Flags in their forties.

And so the Flags became Tasks second full time lodge, nosing out the Oaks, Darcy's second create-a-full-time-lodge project by two months.

Around the lodge system, others struck out on their own. If the building the lodge cleaned was on a bus line, and most of them were, individual workers could go in early or come home late by themselves. They could work along with their part time lodge mates for four hours and put in an additional four hours besides. They might miss a lodge meeting now and then, but most of them preferred work to meetings anyway. And if their lodge mates wanted them to attend certain meetings, they could change the meeting schedule.

Within three years, one third of lodge residents were working full time and loving it. The director figured it was mostly his idea except for the inspiration he got from crotchety old Lou, whose complaint had started the director thinking. But Darcy figured that Silas was the real hero.

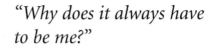

"Why does it always have to be me?"

Alan Kovac
Diamond Lodge

CHAPTER TWELVE

THE RELUCTANT CHAIR

Alan hated the lodge. He had been forced into it against his will.

That was the story of his life; forced into this, forced into that, never any real choices. His life had started poorly and gone downhill from there.

Alan was born at Mendota State Hospital. Nowdays it's rare for a woman to have a baby while a patient in a state facility; and if one did she would be transferred to the maternity ward at a local hospital for the delivery. But in those days, Mendota used to have four or five live births a year. Earlier still, babies born at Mendota were whisked off for adoption and mothers told that they were stillborn. The State was slightly more protective of Alan's mother's rights. Alan was whisked off to a foster home and his mother told she could apply for custody after she established herself in the community.

Alan met his mother several times growing up. She lived in

Minneapolis off and on, but she never seemed to "establish" herself enough to get custody. So Alan grew up in foster homes, several of them. Most of the placements lasted from a few months to a couple of years. The longest was four years.

Alan attended many different schools. He became good at making friends. He was small for his age, so sometimes at a new school the local bully would start to pick on him. But somehow Alan always knew what to say. Pretty soon, Alan was the school bully's best friend. Alan was shy around girls when he was growing up, but the girls liked him. Even most teachers found a warm spot in their heart for this ragamuffin kid with the hard luck story.

Alan never graduated from high school. He was pretty fair at math and real good at shop, but English and history were his downfall. He could read when he had to; it just didn't interest him much. He lettered in wrestling his sophomore year, but his interest in wrestling wasn't enough to keep him in school once he turned sixteen.

At seventeen, Alan and several buddies got caught with a carload of beer and some grass. His buddies were put on probation and sent home to their parents. Alan got sent to a home for incorrigible youth until his eighteenth birthday.

At eighteen, no longer a ward of the court, Alan shared a series of apartments with a series of friends. He held several part-time jobs. His favorite was at the carwash where everybody clowned around a lot, but it was open only in nice weather. And one by one, Alan's buddies enlisted in the service, entered trade school or college, or moved away. The girls he knew were getting married to other guys. For the first time in his life, Alan felt lonely.

A set of his foster parents, a family he had lived with when he was fourteen, offered to help him out. He could live with them, paying minimal rent, if he enrolled as a full time student in the local vo-tech. They would help him with the paperwork and any reading that came up, and he could get a part-time job to cover the tuition. He agreed, and enrolled to become a machinist.

Alan loved machinery and was a quick learner of all the hands-on stuff. The only problem with becoming a machinist was there was more science and more reading than he expected. He had a very difficult time concentrating on any form of book work. His now-unofficial foster parents were eager to help when they had time, but even with their help he couldn't focus for more than a few minutes without becoming restless.

And his foster parents couldn't take his tests for him. Alan never passed one during the seven months he attended vo-tech.

In addition to his concentration problems, Alan was beginning to experience brief periods of unusual behavior. In the middle of doing something, he would just stop. People around him would ask him what he was doing, but other than an occasional grunting noise, Alan would not respond. These spells would last from a few seconds to an hour or so. Afterwards Alan would return more or less to normal. He was aware that he had lost contact with the outside world, but he couldn't explain it. His foster parents took him to see a doctor who diagnosed schizo-affective disorder.

Alan was put on Lithobid and encouraged to try something less stressful than studying to be a machinist. His foster parents took him to see a counselor at the state Department of Vocational Rehabilitation. The counselor recommended vocational evaluation at a program called GROW. The evaluation concluded that he was a good candidate for long-term sheltered employment. As luck would have it, long-term sheltered employment was a service offered by GROW.

Alan hadn't wanted to see a doctor, he hadn't wanted to take Lithobid, he hadn't asked for a vocational evaluation, and he especially hadn't wanted to work at a place like GROW, where most of the workers were retarded. He wasn't a great reader, but he considered himself to be of average intelligence, definitely not retarded. Lacking other options, however, he went to work at GROW, and did well there.

As a Production Assistant, it was Alan's job to check out the equipment in his area at the beginning of each day to ensure that it was working properly. It was also his responsibility to ensure the equipment was shut down properly at the end of each day, or during any work stoppage such as lunch or TDR's. "TDR" stood for Temporary Work Reduction.

Sometimes TDR's were due to a shortage of supplies someone had forgotten to order, or an overdue delivery of raw materials. Generally, however, TDR's were caused by insufficient demand for the products GROW manufactured. Usually a TDR lasted only a day or two, but once or twice each year GROW would experience an ETDR: an Extended Temporary Work Reduction. An ETDR could last several weeks. During the years Alan worked at GROW there were two ETDR's which lasted about six months each.

Even an ETDR did not mean a complete shutdown of GROW, however, no matter how much finished product was stacked up in the warehouse. The production lines operated for one hour each morning, even though continued production in the absence of consumer demand tended to aggravate oversupply.

During one of the six month ETDR's, GROW had to rent additional warehouse space to store surplus products. During the other long ETDR, the workers on Alan's crew would assemble emergency road assistance kits for an hour each morning. At the far end of the production area, another crew would disassemble the kits and sort the components. Even most of the retarded people knew the work was meaningless, but assembling and disassembling the same kits was less expensive than renting another warehouse.

One of the reasons GROW could afford to pay two crews to assemble and disassemble the same parts was that, as a sheltered workshop, GROW was exempt from minimum wage laws. Although GROW voluntarily guaranteed all its workers a minimum wage of twenty-five cents per hour, they could have paid as low as one cent per hour and still charged the state for a day of sheltered employment.

GROW compensated its sheltered workers through a piece-rate system. Alan was never the fastest worker on a production line, but he was always well above average. And yet, the whole time he worked at GROW, doing dozens of tasks on dozens of production lines, he never earned more than two dollars per hour. Although he was willing and able to work full time, and often did, he rarely took home over $50 for a week's work.

Despite his initial reluctance and the chronic low pay, he enjoyed working at GROW. As usual, Alan was very popular and made lots of friends, including some of the retarded people. Alan always felt sorry for the underdog, so he was very patient about listening to sad stories. He never offered advice until people asked for it, and when they did he had a knack for turning the question back to them. People seemed to feel better about themselves after talking to him.

One of the people who took an interest in Alan was Cheryl. She was officially retarded, but just barely. She read better than Alan, for example, but didn't always understand what she read. He was still shy around girls, so when her flirting and hinting didn't work, she asked him out. Pretty soon they were dating steady, and a few months later Cheryl was pregnant.

Cheryl's parents didn't like Alan and they wanted her to have an abortion. But they were only parents, not legal guardians. Cheryl was a legal adult and she wanted to get married, stay home, raise a family. Alan did not especially want to get married, but when the critical moment came, he said, "I do."

They had a son, Robert. Four years later they had another, little Andrew.

Besides Alan's check, they got welfare for the boys, and Cheryl's parents helped out. But it still wasn't enough. Eventually Alan quit his job at GROW and took a job as a caretaker/handyman at the trailer park they lived in. Even so, it was hard to make ends meet. Their phone kept getting shut off, and sometimes their electricity. Every time Alan thought they had finally climbed out of debt, the unexpected would go wrong: car repair or something.

Robert was a nice kid, but kind of rowdy. They started him in kindergarten a year late, so he was bigger and more aggressive than most of the other children. Out on the playground one day, Robert pushed another boy down. Alan was certain Robert hadn't meant to hurt anyone, but the boy hit his head when he fell and had to go to the hospital. The boy was okay, but the school made a big deal out of Robert having pushed him.

Soon afterwards, a social worker from the County came to see them about "how Robert was doing in school." She asked a lot of questions about the trailer park, and finally got around to the incident at school. Alan told her Robert hadn't meant to hurt the other boy, but she said they would have to let a court decide. Alan couldn't imagine the court would send six-year-old Robert to prison for pushing a kid, but he was worried. He tried to call the parents of the other boy so that Robert could apologize, but they never called back.

When they got to court, nobody even mentioned the boy that Robert knocked down. The social worker did most of the talking. Alan and Cheryl had difficulty understanding her because she used big words.

The conclusion of the hearing was the biggest shock of Alan's life. The judge decided to remove Robert from his parent's custody, and put him in a foster home. Alan was stunned. He and Cheryl loved Robert and had done the best they could to provide for him. Alan had no idea this outcome was even a possibility. He cried uncontrollably and had to be helped from the courtroom. He was inconsolable for months, often even neglecting his duties around the trailer park, where he was usually so responsible.

At first, Robert came home on supervised visits, but Alan and Cheryl never regained custody. Approximately eighteen months after Robert was removed from their home, another hearing was held. This time little Andrew was removed. Losing Andrew was less of a shock because Alan understood the proceedings better and he knew it could happen. He even kind of expected it based on what had happened to Robert.

Although it was less of a surprise, losing little Andrew was no easier to accept. Alan didn't cry in court, but when he and Cheryl returned to their trailer the silence was deafening. For two days he wouldn't leave the trailer and hardly spoke to Cheryl. On the third day, while Cheryl was at the store, Alan drank a bottle of strychnine.

When he woke up in the hospital, he didn't immediately understand where he was. When he learned his stomach had been pumped out and he was going to live, he was as angry as he had ever been his entire life. Once he was physically stable, they transferred him to a psych ward. He had heard his friends from GROW talk about psych wards, but he had never been in one before. People were nicer to him than he expected; they even cheered him up a bit.

Once he returned home, however, the situation was bleak. He was still in debt and the boys were still gone. Cheryl blamed him for everything. Cheryl, Robert, and Andrew had been the only bright spots in his miserable life. Now the boys were gone, probably for good, and Cheryl hated him. Four months after drinking the strychnine, with Cheryl away overnight at her parents, Alan ran a garden hose from the tailpipe of his car in through a window into his bedroom.

The six-pack he had drunk helped him get to sleep. He dozed off, smelling the car exhaust, thinking he had solved his problems forever. All of which was forgotten when he got up in the middle of the night to urinate. As he stumbled back to bed, he noticed the always drafty trailer was much colder than usual. He saw the open window and the hose. He stared out the window and saw that the hose was still duct-taped to the tailpipe of the car. Then he remembered the car was really low on gas.

His first instinct was to unhook the hose from the car so no one would catch on, and try again the next night. But it was cold out and he had a hangover. He pushed the hose out the window, shut the window and went back to bed. Cheryl's father brought her home the next morning before Alan got up. He saw the hose attached to the tailpipe and coiled loosely beneath the bedroom window. He guessed the general idea and half expected to find Alan dead. Alan was alive, so he took him to the hospital.

While Alan was in the hospital the second time, Cheryl's parents talked her into divorcing him. Now he was completely alone. He had lost track of his mother, lost custody of his sons, and his soon-to-be ex-wife wouldn't return his phone calls.

Alan was treated with a new antidepressant called Prozac. When the doctor decided he was stable, they discharged him to a residential program called the Community of Life Academy, popularly known as "COLA." He was allowed to collect his worldly possessions from the trailer park. They filled up two plastic garbage bags.

COLA was a licensed treatment facility for people with mental illness. Besides individual therapy twice a week, group therapy four times a week, and recreation six days a week, there were lots of activities, none of which interested Alan very much. He slept eighteen to twenty hours per day, getting up only for meals and occasionally to take his Prozac. Looking back, Alan says the two-and-a-half years he spent at COLA was the best time of his life. There was plenty to eat, a nice warm bed, and nobody hassled him. He would still be there today if they had let him stay.

The only problem with COLA was that it was intended to be a twelve month program. After approximately twelve months, people were supposed to move on to independent apartments and live happily ever after. The staff at COLA taught residents to cook and do laundry, and even helped them find an apartment. Best of all, the counselors talked to them about their mental illness, so they could develop the insight to recognize delusional thoughts.

As usual, Alan was popular with staff and residents during his waking hours. On the rare occasions that he cooked or went to a recreational activity, he was invariably good at it. He didn't care much for the therapy, though; talking about his miserable life only made it seem worse. Fortunately all of the program activities at COLA were optional. Ninety percent of the time, Alan chose to sleep. He really liked COLA.

His counselor would often suggest that Alan's lifestyle, sleeping all day, was boring and unproductive. Alan said he did not mind. His counselor suggested that sleeping all the time actually made a person more depressed, but Alan explained that asleep was the only time he wasn't depressed. About the fifteenth month, his assigned counselor started talking to him about his "discharge plan." Alan never argued, he just listened. About the eighteenth month, his counselor started making appointments for him to see various apartments. Alan never went. He knew he had a good deal going.

Eventually, the staff at COLA gave up on sending Alan to an apartment, but they were under pressure from the mental health department to move him on. They tried to get him into a nursing home, but they couldn't prove he was sick enough.

At some point in the discussions, Alan mentioned that he liked to work, especially with machines. The idea seemed ridiculous to the COLA staff since employment usually proved too stressful for even their highest-functioning residents. They couldn't imagine Alan getting out of bed often enough to hold a job, but they were desperate. There was one mental health program in town, Tasks Unlimited, which expected their residents to work. The COLA staff knew Alan wouldn't succeed at Tasks, but they figured they didn't have to tell Tasks. The records they kept primarily documented the problems people caused, and Alan had never caused any, so the records they sent Tasks made him look pretty good. Alan didn't want to go to Tasks, but as usual he had no choice.

When he moved to Tasks Lodge Training Program, Alan thought he had moved from heaven to hell. The work was fine, but the rest of it sucked.

Breakfast was at 8 a.m. The first day, a guy in a gray t-shirt came to get him about 8:01 a.m. Alan told the guy he wasn't interested in breakfast. The guy grunted something and left. The guy came back about 8:05 a.m. Alan ignored him. About 8:06, six guys came into his tiny room. He jumped out of bed thinking some emergency was occurring, "Was the house on fire? Had somebody died?" He recognized the gray t-shirt, but a black guy in front was barking at him about getting up. "Helluva big staff," thought Alan (only it later turned out that they were all trainees, not staff).

He found himself in the dining room before any of his questions were answered. The emergency turned out to be that breakfast was ten minutes late because of Alan.

A guy named Ray, who was staff, was sitting at a desk in a room adjacent to the dining room. After getting a cup of coffee, Alan approached him to explain that he did not care much for the storm trooper tactics.

"Tell it to the group," he said.

"Huh?," said Alan.

"If you didn't like the way your wake-up was handled, talk to the group about it. There will be a group meeting at 10 a.m.."

"The point is," Alan explained, "I didn't need to be woken up at all. I'm tired and I don't usually eat breakfast anyway."

"Not my problem," Ray said. "Take it up with the group at 10 a.m.."

Alan looked toward the dining room where people were eating breakfast. They were not paying any attention to Alan now.

"Leave me alone, " he said to no one in particular, "I'm going back to bed."

About 8:45 a.m., before he had even gotten back to sleep, the gray t-shirt was in his room again talking about meds.

"Tell the staff I'll take them when I get up."

"Won't work," said the gray t-shirt.

"No, really, I promise. I don't have any problem taking my meds."

"Nobody will get their meds until you're there."

"You're joking!"

After Alan got to know Jack of the gray t-shirt, and Silas, the black guy, he came to realize that they didn't joke about house rules. It turned out Jack had specifically been assigned responsibility for giving Alan the attention which Alan considered harassment. "New Admit Buddy," they called it.

There was no lock on his bedroom door, so he abandoned even trying to go back to bed. He tried to lie down on the living room couch. Silas told him he could recline but he had to keep his feet on the floor. (As annoying as they were, Alan found he had too much in common with Jack and Silas to hate them; they were losers, but who was he to talk?)

The whole first day was like that. Every five minutes there was something Alan had to do. And if he didn't do it on time, someone was in his face about it. Alan was finally allowed to go to bed about 9:45 p.m., after almost four hours of real janitorial work at a contract site, followed by supper, the third group meeting of the day, during which he could hardly hold his head up, and evening meds. A bed never felt so good.

The next day was the same, "Do this, do that, and hurry up about it." And every day afterwards for over four months. He hated everything about the Lodge Training Program. He hadn't wanted to come and he hated it. He was tired all the time and he fantasized about running away and going back to COLA where he could get some rest. He got up when he had to, however, and did what had to be done.

Alan hated the staff, especially Ray. Ray wouldn't confront him directly. If Ray saw him doing something wrong he would write it down and later Alan would have to answer for it to the group. But Alan didn't get as many of the dreaded "notes" written about him as the other trainees did. As a result, he quickly got promoted to the top "step level" which meant he enjoyed certain privileges the other trainees didn't have. One of these privileges was that he was eligible to be elected Chairman of the group. Alan didn't consider this to be much of a privilege. For one thing, the Chairman had to read the "notes" aloud at the group meeting and he didn't like to read. Worse yet, the Chairman had to lead the discussion of what the special punishment should be for each infraction. He felt that people with mental problems had suffered enough already; he hated to see them punished at all, especially for minor infractions. He thought Ray was running some kind of a scam, making the trainees discipline each other. He refused to be Chairman.

Ray explained that taking on leadership responsibility was one of the requirements for graduating to a lodge. Apparently lodges were different from the Lodge Training Program in that instead of the staff being in the next room they were across town somewhere. But it worked the same as far as Alan could figure; the residents were trained to make each other do what the staff wanted them to do. He had had enough of other people making decisions for him: foster parents, the staff at GROW, his ex-wife, the owner of the trailer park, the people that took his kids away. He wanted no part of it.

The only part of the Lodge Training Program he liked was the work. The trainees got to work as janitors about four hours a day. Most of the work was similar to stuff he had done before, and he was pretty good at it. After a while, he got to liking janitorial work quite a bit. Like GROW, Tasks had a sub-minimum permit, but their math must have been different because Alan tested just barely below minimum wage. They told him that when he graduated to the lodge he would be guaranteed minimum wage, and might earn even twice that much.

Except when he was working, he thought about his kids. Whenever he thought about his kids he got depressed. He was still taking Prozac but it didn't seem to help. Dr. Bob switched him to Effexor, which seemed to work better. Still, sleeping was his only refuge. He wished he were back at COLA where everybody left him alone.

After three months, Ray said that Alan should move on to a

lodge. Alan adamantly refused. Ray argued with him. Ray tried to get him to go visit a couple of lodges. Alan refused to visit.

"The whole point of the Lodge Training Program," Ray explained, "is to train people for lodges. Once you've been trained, you are supposed to go."

Alan said, "I thought the point of the program was to torture people with a lot of dumb rules."

"Name a rule you think is dumb," said a clearly annoyed Ray.

"Well, you said there was a rule that I couldn't go to a lodge until I became one of the leaders around here, telling other people what to do. That's the dumbest rule I ever heard. Besides that, I am not a leader, and now you say I can go to the lodge anyway, so you don't even follow your own dumb rule."

"You are a leader," said Ray.

"Am not."

"The whole group looks up to you. They would elect you Chair if you let them."

"I won't go to a lodge," he said. "I want to have my own apartment."

Ray was frustrated. He hated it when people wanted to go to apartments instead of lodges. Finally he said, "Fine. Get yourself an apartment. You won't be happy living by yourself."

"Will too," Alan said.

Another month went by. Alan had done nothing about finding an apartment. Ray made him visit the Painters Lodge.

"It was okay," he said afterwards, "but I'm not going to live there."

"You have to live somewhere," Ray insisted. "You can't live here for ever."

"I'm gonna get an apartment."

"So get one. We're giving you thirty days notice."

The thirty days went by pretty fast. On several occasions

Alan swore he would look for an apartment the next day. He never did.

Ray kept reminding him, "The clock is ticking."

"I never have time," Alan complained, "because the schedule here is so busy."

"You know the weekend activities are only required for people on step level one," Ray pointed out. "You're on step level four. You can come and go as you like all weekend."

"All right," he said, "I'll go out this weekend and find an apartment."

Two weeks later, the thirty days was up. Alan had not received a rule violation note in five weeks. Neither had he looked for an apartment.

"Pack your stuff," Ray told him at breakfast. "You're moving to the Painters Lodge today."

"I won't go," Alan said.

"You have to," Ray said. "We have a new trainee arriving this afternoon and he needs your bed."

"I want my own apartment."

"Fine," Ray said. "Today you move to the Painters Lodge. Tomorrow you look for an apartment."

Sixteen months after moving to the Painters, Alan, still the sympathetic listener and everyone's buddy, was elected chairman of the lodge. He protested loudly, but the vote was otherwise unanimous. The rules of the Painters Lodge called for one-year terms, but after Alan was re-elected for his third term (again unanimously), they kind of let the election process slide. He entered his fourth and fifth year as chair without the formality of an election.

He would probably be the chairman of the Painters Lodge to this day, except that halfway through his sixth year at the

Painters he moved to the Diamond Lodge. The Diamonds were a new lodge exclusively for people working full time. Darcy, the Tasks Unlimited social worker, held a meeting to recruit volunteers for the experiment. Alan went to the meeting because Calvin and Phil were going. He put his name on a list along with everybody else, but he didn't expect anything to come of it.

Darcy met with him later to review his financial situation. She explained that working full time wouldn't change his net income much. He would earn more, of course, but he would lose his Disability. It all came out about even.

"So, what do you think?" Darcy asked him. "Do you want to try this new lodge where you will have to work full time?"

Alan thought that it sounded pretty dumb to work twice as hard and not really get paid for it. It reminded him of those poor fools at GROW who worked for 25 cents an hour. Not that he really minded working. He preferred not to do anything at all, but if he had to do something, there were worse things than working. He also thought to himself that Darcy's question was a hoax. Since when did anyone care what he thought?

But he didn't share any of these thoughts with Darcy. His exact answer was, "Whatever."

So Alan was selected to be one of the guinea pigs. He objected of course, but Darcy told him it was too late to back out. To make matters worse, the Diamonds also elected him chair.

The first couple of months were hard because none of the Diamonds were accustomed to working eight-hour shifts. But after a while Alan decided it was about the same. He had worked full time at GROW (although for a lot less money), then part time at the Painters Lodge, and now full time again. Either way, he was always tired and always broke.

Darcy made him send several letters to Social Security. He never really tried to read them, but according to Warren, who was sending similar letters, they were demanding that Social Security stop sending him money. Social Security kept sending him checks and letters which said, according to Warren, that he could keep the money, but Darcy wouldn't let him cash the checks.

He and Warren figured that Darcy was running some sort of scam, and one day she was going to disappear with the Diamond's cash box and thousands of dollars worth of government checks. But finally, he got a letter from Social Security which (according to Darcy and Warren) said that he had better return all the checks or they would send him to prison. Darcy wanted him to thank her for advising him not to spend the money, but Alan figured she had gotten him into the whole mess in the first place.

Now she is making him take reading lessons. Alan hates the reading lessons. He says the two years he slept at COLA was the best time of his life.

"Some people don't have any idea what stuff is worth."

Carl Shagauboy
Diamond Lodge

CHAPTER THIRTEEN

GARAGE SALE ART

Carl was one-quarter Indian. His father was one-quarter Wisconsin Ojibwa and his mother one-quarter Grand Rapids Chippewa. Not as much of a mixed marriage as it sounds, since both tribes were of the Anishinabe people; "Chippewa" and "Ojibwa" being names misapplied by early European invaders. Today, many of the back-to-our-roots Anishinabes, both Chippewa and Ojibwa, just call themselves "Nabs."

Carl had actually been born on the reservation where his mother had people, but his parents had a farm about twenty miles north of the Rez.

His childhood was pretty normal for a north-woods farm boy. He went to school when his mother made him, worked around the farm when his father made him, and spent the rest of his time in the woods and on the lakes with his buddies. He had one friend who was part Nab and a boy cousin about his

203

age on the Rez, but most of his friends were an Iron Range mix of Finns and assorted Slavs. They learned to fish and hunt and smoke and drink and drive a car in that order, basic education complete by age twelve.

Carl was an average student in school, a little better than average in art class, but from the beginning he excelled at something else. He had a knack for trading: for buying low and selling high. He could trade a baseball card for a jackknife for a fishing rod for an outboard that didn't run for one that did for a snowmobile for a pickup truck. All in one day.

Cars and trucks became his passion. He acquired his first at age thirteen, and nearly twenty had passed through his hands by the time he got his legal driving permit at sixteen. His favorite was a '73 Delta 88 four-door. It had a 455 cube, 400 horsepower engine. He acquired it in trade for stuff that cost him practically nothing. He repaired a little trim, pounded out a couple of dents, and repainted it Mercedes-Cocoa-Brown-Metal-Flake. He sold it for $3,000. His life ambition at the time was to own his own dealership, Cadillac perhaps, or some other luxury car.

Carl ended up at the Diamond Lodge, moving there from Bay Lodge for the chance to work full time. The Diamond Lodge was a sprawling ranch house, converted from a double bungalow, on a quiet suburban cul-de-sac. The one thing that bothered him about his new lodge was the decor. While members were each responsible for their own bedroom, Tasks Unlimited had decorated and furnished the common areas, and Tasks' taste was sterile. White walls and sturdy, nondescript furniture. Tasks talked up the home-like nature of the lodge, but to Carl's eye, the house looked like a hospital day room.

When the Diamonds moved in, the big brick house on the

corner leading into the cul-de-sac had a "for sale" sign on the lawn. The old lady who had lived there had moved to a nursing home, apparently not to return. After the house sold, the old lady's daughter and daughter-in-law had a big sale to get rid of all her stuff. The sale started on a Thursday morning. Carl had noticed a sign about some sort of sale, but he hadn't paid much attention until that morning when he noticed all the commotion. Cars were parked all the way into and around the cul-de-sac, and there was a steady stream of people hurrying in and out of the big brick house. The Diamonds didn't go to work until 11am, so Carl decided to check it out.

Everything in the house (really nice stuff, the lady obviously had good taste) was for sale. But Carl couldn't believe the pricing system. A color television which worked was tagged $10. A portable radio was marked $2 — the batteries in it were worth more than that. Mismatched dishes, some of them without so much as a chip or a scratch, were going for 25 cents. On the other hand, there was a complete set of eight of the ugliest dishes he had ever seen (a couple of which were cracked) for $600. And a lamp was tagged $2,000. He thought at first that the tags were written incorrectly, that the sellers wanted $6.00 for the dishes and $20.00 for the lamp. But then two women got into a argument about a small table, which was tagged $250 (Carl assumed $2.50). One woman said she saw it first. The other woman told the seller she would pay three hundred dollars! For a little table!

There was definitely something weird going on, and a lot of money changing hands. Carl didn't know how it worked, or why, but he figured he could make some money trading with people who sold undamaged plates for 25 cents and sets of damaged ones for $600.

He left that day with the television, the radio, four matching cereal bowls, two brand new cookie sheets, five assorted jello

molds, a brand new pair of Adidas, a barely worn pair of Dan
Post cowgirl boots, forty or fifty dollars worth of canned goods,
and a wheelbarrow in good condition to carry it all home.
All for $34. He later resold the television to his new lodge mate
Silas for $30, the Adidas to Ed at Hiawatha for $40, the wheelbarrow to the Diamonds next-door neighbor for $30, traded
the boots to a girl-cousin for an aluminum canoe, donated the
cereal bowls, cookie sheets, jello molds, and can goods to the
Diamond Lodge, and kept the radio for his own use.

Carl discovered to his delight that there were a lot of sales
in this middle-class, single-family neighborhood, especially in
the spring and summer. It was a neighborhood tradition.
Almost everyone participated. Every spring, each housewife
would go through her house, round up everything she hadn't
used recently, carry it out to the garage, and put a tag on it.
Then she would have a sale. Sometimes the husbands were in
on it, too.

The first summer he was cash-poor a couple of times when
he stumbled across something really cool, so he tried to swap
something he had purchased earlier in the day for it. But his
new neighbors had no interest in trading, no matter how good a
deal he offered.

That was how he came to understand the point of suburban garage sales. The real goal was to exchange an item of
uncertain utility for something of guaranteed utility, *i.e.*, an
empty space in their closet, garage or attic. People had houses
full of stuff, but they kept buying more stuff. Pretty soon even
the biggest houses were full, but still they bought more stuff.
People were forced to sell off the old stuff to make room for the
new stuff they were buying. Small items like jewelry, he learned,
weren't especially good values except for the occasional deceased
estate sale, because they didn't command space. Large items,
like snow-blowers, cars and sofas could be purchased for practi-

cally nothing. People would almost pay Carl to take away a hide-a-bed, even if it was brand new.

Sometimes the old stuff was worn or broken or obsolete, but often not. Frequently the old stuff had only been used a couple of times and was just like new. Occasionally, the "old" stuff had never been used at all. People seemed to buy stuff they didn't want for reasons they couldn't explain; then they were too lazy or too embarrassed to return it. But they weren't too lazy or too embarrassed to resell it to their neighbors. More than once Carl saw a one-of-a-kind item for sale in one garage and the next summer the same item, still unused, was for sale in a different garage three blocks away.

Better yet, they weren't selling stuff to raise money, as people on the Rez did. They just wanted to get rid of it. They often didn't care about the price. Once in a while, someone who knew what a dollar was worth would put realistic prices on things and refuse to bargain. But nobody would buy anything, so the sale would be a failure, and the person would never try again. More commonly, people would tag like-new items for twenty-five percent of their retail value and settle for ten percent. At first Carl thought they were all stupid. He was almost furtive in closing a deal, as though someone was going to notice and void the sale. But it wasn't necessarily that they didn't know the value of things. Sometimes an item had an original price tag still on it and Carl could still buy it for ten percent of retail.

Already at Bay Lodge, Carl had acquired a reputation as the guy who could get you a cheap car. Now he became known throughout the whole Tasks Unlimited lodge system as a guy who could get all kinds of stuff. He could procure not only personal items, but also stuff for the lodges. There were eleven lodges at the time, and they were constantly in need of beds, dressers, appliances, rugs, couches, dining room sets, lawn mowers, snow blowers, tools, and housewares.

At first he would buy things he knew were really good deals, confident that he could cover his cost plus a modest profit from one lodge or another. As his reputation grew, he shopped more for specific needs as lodges began to place orders. "The Lilacs are redecorating," JoEllen would say. "We need a sofa and matching love seat to go with our new bluish-gray-green living room carpet, and some rattan furniture for the three season porch. We've got $500 to spend." They knew they could get better quality for their money going through Carl than at a discount furniture store.

As he became more familiar with the other lodges, he developed ideas about specific needs which went beyond lodge-initiated requests. While visiting a lodge, he would notice something which needed replacement or upgrading or something they didn't have at all, like maybe a microwave. Especially he noticed the need for artwork.

His formal training in art ended with a couple of community college classes, but he knew what he liked and didn't like. The thing he didn't like the most was bare walls. Except for dogs playing poker or Elvis on black velvet, he considered any kind of framed art to be an improvement over bare walls. His two special interests were French impressionists, popular with the female and co-ed lodges, and combat planes in flight, which appealed to the all-male lodges.

Tasks took a bare-bones approach to setting up lodges, and except for Bay Lodge, because of Carl having lived there, none of the lodge groups had really addressed esthetics in the sense of artwork. By Carl's fourth anniversary at Diamond Lodge, the walls of most lodges were saturated with artwork, some beyond maximum esthetics. It took a determined lodge to preserve even one-half of a bare wall in the face of his insistence that they fill it up with an excellent Monet print costing less than the value of the frame.

Carl carried an image of all the walls of all the common areas of all the lodges in his mind's eye. When he came across a decent piece of art at a give-away price, he would run these images through his head until he came to the perfect wall for this particular piece, even if it meant moving existing pieces to other lodges.

Purchasing the art at a bargain price was a piece of cake. The bigger the piece the more eager the sellers were to get rid of it. Turning of profit on the resale to a lodge was more difficult because few lodge members appreciated the value of art. He once bought a handsomely framed print worth at least $150 for only $15, and offered it to the Spirit Lodge, who had a perfect spot to hang it, for $30. But the Spirits grumbled about paying $30, not because they didn't like the picture, but just because they didn't have a clue what it was really worth. And because Chuckie thought they had enough art already.

As the lodges reached the saturation point, Carl gradually gave up on the idea of making a profit reselling art to lodges. He didn't really need the money; between his full time job with Tasks Unlimited and the profits he made reselling non-art garage-sale items to individual lodge members, he was in fat city. But his desire to fill the walls of the lodges with art transcended his obsession with profit. He felt that art, even mediocre art, was uplifting.

His favorite painting, which hung over the mantel in the Diamond Lodge, was of a squadron of F-15's in formation slicing through a cloudy dawn. He really admired the way the unknown painter, "Wescott" or "Wiscolt" or something like that, had captured the power and thrill of the F-15's on a sunrise raid. It made him feel good about being an American every time he looked at it, and he looked at it every day.

There were days he woke up feeling strangely anxious, worried about things he knew he had no control over. When this got bad, he would sit and stare at the F-15's. Gradually his confidence and his ability to focus on immediate tasks at hand would return. The F-15's were a symbol of American power and success and he was proud to be an American. His role in American society was small compared to the F-15's, but somehow it was all woven together. If it was his day to take out the recycling then he had to do it. In some small way, he depended on the F-15's, and the F-15's depended on him.

He knew that other lodge members, even the Diamonds, did not understand this interdependence the way he did. They certainly didn't understand art. But he wanted to help the others, and he felt it was his responsibility to contribute however he could. He felt if he put enough art on enough lodge walls, every lodge member would have at least one picture which did for them what the F-15's did for him.

"We finally figured it out, women are trouble."

Darryl Wesley
Spirit Lodge

CHAPTER FOURTEEN

THE TOGA PARTY

The director of Tasks Unlimited was invited to address a national symposium of Fairweather Lodges on the topic of lodge rules. His hypothesis was that neither sponsoring agencies nor supervising professionals should make rules for lodges because investing total rulemaking authority in the participating membership was a more effective form of governance. In preparation for his speech, he asked each of Tasks' lodges to give him a copy of their rules. He noticed that all the lodges had some sort of rule, or rules, about sex, except for Spirit Lodge. And all of the lodges except the Lilacs had a rule or rules about alcohol.

He sent notes to Spirit and the Lilacs asking if perhaps they had forgotten to include those rules in the lists they had submitted. Both lodges assured him there had been no oversight. They simply did not have rules in those areas. He sent them both notes asking if they didn't think they SHOULD have rules in those areas, given the complexity of human behavior and so forth. Neither lodge responded before he left for the conference.

When he returned, he found he had received a lengthy communication from the Lilacs, but still nothing from Spirit Lodge. He set the note from the Lilacs aside to read when he had caught up with all his other pressing business, but immediately sent a follow-up note to the Spirits, demanding a response.

Spirit Lodge responded with an inquiry: "What does our rule about sex have to say?"

The director responded, "It is not up to me or any other staff to set your rules. The only people who can do that are the voting members of Spirit Lodge. You are the lodge. It is entirely your responsibility to set the rules, interpret the rules, enforce the rules, and change the rules if necessary. You are not required to have rules about sex, but given the volatile nature of the topic, I think it would be prudent. I merely ask that you send Tasks a copy, so that we may refer to it if anyone ever asks."

Spirit Lodge responded, "Here is our rule: Sex is a good thing. Members are encouraged to have sex whenever, wherever, and with whoever (sic) they can, as frequently as they can (given the impotence causing side-effects of the meds they make us take)."

The director responded, "Nice rule. If you were all on Mellaril, I would be less concerned about this, but I happen to know most of you are not. You can have a free-love policy if you want, but I would like some assurance that you have at least considered the following potential problems:

What about privacy?

What about disease?

What about unintended pregnancy?

What about your reputation in the immediate neighborhood? In the Lodge Community?

What about homosexual acts between two members of the

Spirit Lodge on the rec-room couch while the rest of you are trying to watch TV?"

Less than two weeks later, the director received the following response, "We have changed our rule. The new rule is: No sex ever, under any circumstances, either in the Spirit Lodge or involving Spirit members."

The director was not amused. Skilled mental health professional that he was, he easily recognized passive aggressive behavior. He called the Spirit Lodge and spoke to Darryl, the Lodge Chairman. He demanded a meeting. Darryl explained that Spirit Lodge meetings were held every Thursday at 11 am, and he was welcome to attend anytime he chose. The following Thursday, the director appeared at Spirit Lodge. He demanded to know why the Spirits were jacking him around on a perfectly reasonable request.

The members of Spirit Lodge weren't quite sure what to say. They were familiar with the term "jacking around," but they couldn't understand how it applied in this context. In what sense had they "jacked him around?"

Chris was the first to figure it out. "You think we weren't serious?"

"Obviously you weren't serious."

"Why is that obvious?"

"You start with an all-sex, all-the-time rule. Then just because I ask a couple of questions, perfectly reasonable questions, you change to a no-sex, not-ever rule. You're jacking me around."

This analysis seemed to startle Spirit Lodge. No one said anything for a while. Eventually, Darryl spoke up. "Your memo ... the questions you asked ... didn't really have anything ... I mean they weren't ... That wasn't why we changed the rules."

Now the director was slightly startled. "Well then, why did you change the rules?"

This time the delay in answering was even longer, uncomfortably long. If the director could have read eyeballs, translating their movements like hulas, he could have learned a lot. Each of the five Spirit members seemed to make eye contact with each of the other four, a randomly choreographed eyeball dance. The director could see that his question had started this dance, but he had no clue what it meant.

Again, it was Darryl who finally cleared his throat softly. The dancing stopped. Now everyone's eyes were fixed on Darryl and he realized it was too late to back out of saying something. "The other rule wasn't working out." Again, a silent pause, but not as long because all eyes remained fixed on Darryl, the pressure of which made it impossible for him not to continue. "We had a bad experience."

The director thought to himself, "Something blew up in their faces; one big incident scared the crap out of them." He felt as he did watching a horror movie when the music comes up all weird and he just knew something grisly was going to jump out of the closet. Something terrible had happened which was going to embarrass the whole lodge program, and maybe even threaten its future. On his watch. Just as at the movies, he had an urge to turn his head, to get up and leave before the closet opened, but just as in the movies, he could not.

But he never figured out what really happened. He left Spirit Lodge that day undecided whether there had been one terrible incident they were determined to keep secret, or whether Darryl had simply misspoken when he said "a" bad experience. The remainder of the meeting consisted of various members recounting numerous awkward experiences, which they claimed added up to clear cause for the dramatic rule change.

"We added the 'sex is good' rule to the lodge rules," Chris said, hooking his thumb toward the big cork bulletin board on the dining room wall directly behind him. "But Chuckie wrote it in red, with a big felt-tip marker. It was the first thing you saw when you walked in here. You could read it from the living room even. Gloria took one look at it and asked, 'What does that mean?' I explained to her that it didn't really mean much of anything. But she got all excited about it, said she wasn't into anything kinky. I said, 'Gloria, Sugar, this doesn't have anything to do with you and me.' But she said, 'I'm not coming over any more. I'm not comfortable around a bunch of perverts.' What a moron," Chris said staring over at Chuckie.

"I wasn't the one," Chuckie said, looking at Darryl, "who rented twelve triple-x videos the same weekend and monopolized the VCR running them back-to-back till we couldn't even tell which one we were watching and even then we never got to see all twelve."

"Yeah," said Darryl, "at least I paid for them. Not like those 900 calls that someone won't admit making."

"What are you looking at me for?" asked Dean. "I told you it wasn't me. And it wasn't my girlfriend, by the way, who told the Lilacs we were all a bunch of perverts."

"That's cause you don't have a girlfriend," said Darryl.

"Well, I might have if Gloria wasn't bad-mouthing us all over the place."

"Gloria didn't have anything to do with that. And you are never going to score with Susie Q. anyway."

"That's not her name. And what do you know?"

"I know who made those 900 calls."

"Prove it," demanded Dean.

There was a pause, but Darryl didn't answer. After a minute, Silas spoke up. "Then there was that deal with Wally; bringing his girlfriend over here to do what they're not allowed to do at the Painters."

"They didn't do anything. They just dropped by for a beer."

"I saw what they were doing."

This went on for a while. The director learned that Spirit Lodge, inspired by the sex-is-good rule, had attempted to hold a toga party. Only no women came, and they all felt stupid.

Darryl seemed to be speaking for the whole lodge as he summed up the conclusion which led to the reversal in rules. "We finally figured it out," he said, "women are trouble."

The director encouraged them to think about changing the no-sex-ever rule to something more reasonable, some kind of middle ground. He got no response. There was very little enthusiasm, at least that day, for discussing rules about sex.

As Darcy had often explained to the director, lodge members had insufficient experience with self-governance. Most had spent years in institutions and group homes where staff made all the rules. While at the Lodge Training Program, prospective lodge members were told by staff there that the lodge rules are made and enforced by the lodge members. And that lodge members are not only treated like adults, and held accountable for their behavior as adults ought to be, but also held accountable for the behavior of their lodge mates, as family members often are. But initially much of the message gets lost in the flood of information about client rights, safety procedures, activity schedules and really important information such as when payday is. To the extent that the message, "You are now your brother's keeper," gets heard at all, the typical response (sometimes spoken aloud, more often thought silently) is, "Sure, and monkeys are going to fly out of my butt, too."

This cynicism is based on the fact that people have been told, "The choice is yours," "We value your input," "You are going to be treated like an adult now," by every institution they've been in, dating back to kindergarten. And it was never true before. To a veteran of the mental health system, the idea of being truly responsible for one's own behavior seems preposterous; and the idea of people with mental illness being held responsible for the behavior of other people with mental illness is beyond preposterous. It is understandable that previously institutionalized people would view this as a scam.

Overcoming the cynicism requires diligent loyalty to the principle of group self-determination. Every time the training staff overrule a decision made by a group of trainees, the process starts all over again. Even in a lodge, where the principle of lodge autonomy is supposed to be well established, it is easy for staff to undermine the process. Even a well-meaning Lodge Coordinator or agency director can subvert the process by failing to trust the group. "The key," Darcy always said, "is remembering that it is more important that the lodge rules are meaningful to the lodge members, than to staff.

But the director had not gotten where he was by being a quick study. Before long, he received a second communication from the Lilacs, which reminded him to read the first. The first read:

"We have had lengthy discussions with regards to the matter you inquired about, as we could not agree at first.

"Three of us are of the tee-totaling persuasion, while three of the girls like to party, just a little. Gloria and JoEllen, for example, are inclined to split a beer every night after work. Except on Fridays when Gloria will drink an entire beer by herself, because JoEllen likes to drink a Peach Wine Cooler on Fridays. Susie doesn't drink at all during the week, but often on Saturday afternoons, or sometimes Sundays, especially if there's a ballgame on TV, she likes a rum and coke, sometimes two. Except in really hot weather when she often likes to drink a gin and tonic, but only if she remembers ahead of time to add a fresh lime or lemon to our grocery list.

"We all agreed with you that these are dangerous patterns. We are especially concerned about our youngest member, Angie, and the example the older girls are setting. She doesn't drink at all now, but her brother was an alcoholic and eventually committed suicide. We would never forgive ourselves if anything like that happened to Angie.

"So we checked around the other lodges, and found several had rules that there could not be any alcohol whatsoever stored or consumed in the lodge. This seems to work at the Hiawatha and Painters Lodges, for example, so we thought it would work for us. We all agreed, even Gloria, JoEllen, and Susie.

"But apparently, some of the boys at the Painters Lodge frequent a nearby bar, and this was exactly what Gloria and JoEllen started doing. Every night after work and after meds, Gloria and JoEllen walked down to 'Tony's on Grand' to have their beer. Although this was better in the sense that they weren't drinking in front of Angie, it was worse in other ways.

"The first night they ordered a bottle of beer and two glasses. The bartender served them what they ordered, but the girls felt that he gave them a very disapproving look. They felt so guilty, they ended up leaving him a 100% tip, which meant they spent as much on the one beer as they would normally spend on a six-pack at the grocery store.

"The next night they each ordered a ten-ounce glass of beer, which was considerably cheaper and did not generate disapproval. But afterward, JoEllen remembered that draft beer gives her hangovers. And sure enough, the next morning she had a terrible headache. She was in such a mood that we all felt terrible and we ran around all morning offering her aspirin, Tylenol, ibuprofen, and whatever else we could think of. We don't want to go through that again.

"So since then, they have each ordered a full bottle of beer. Not only is this more expensive than splitting one at home, they were drinking twice as much as they used to.

*"There is another problem as well. 'Tony's on Grand' is
two blocks away. None of us hesitate to walk to the stores on
Grand and back in the middle of the day, even by ourselves.
But this neighborhood changes at night. And they don't
even head down there until after nine o'clock meds, so it is
always dark when they come home. Gloria says she doesn't
mind, but JoEllen does and the rest of us do, too. None of us
go to bed until they're home each night.*

*"We also worry about two of our girls drinking in a bar
full of strange men. It's all well and good for the Painters to
hang out at bars, but its different for Gloria and JoEllen.
Gloria says she knows how to handle drunks because she
used to work as a barmaid. But that was almost thirty years
ago, and times have changed.*

*"So at our meeting yesterday, we repealed the 'no-alco-
hol' rule, and made the following new ones:*

*"Effective immediately, the Lilac Lodge will have an
additional officer known as the Alcohol Monitor. The
Alcohol Monitor shall be elected by majority vote of the Lilac
Lodge. Every member of the lodge gets one vote whether
they drink or not; every member must vote, whether they
drink or not; everyone is eligible to be the Alcohol Monitor,
whether they drink or not.*

*"The Alcohol Monitor is responsible for monitoring the
storage and consumption of alcohol at the Lilac Lodge. This
includes members and their guests. 'At the lodge' includes
the entire house, the yard, the garage, and the Lilac van even
if it's parked on the street.*

*"The responsibilities of the Alcohol Monitor shall
include, but not be limited to:*

*"Keeping an inventory of all alcohol stored at the lodge,
including amount, type, brand, percentage of alcohol, who
bought it and when, who consumed it and when. In the
case of products such as hard liquor, which have a long
shelf-life even after they've been opened, the Alcohol
Monitor shall be responsible for estimating the volume
remaining.*

"Ensuring that no more than 1.8 oz of alcohol (or the equivalent thereof) is consumed by any member in any twenty-four hour period. (Male guests allowed up to 2.7 oz.)

"Reporting at one of the weekly lodge meetings as to the inventory, consumption patterns, and any problems therewith."

The second communication, which the director received before he had read the first, said:

"We have encountered a couple of glitches with our new rules on alcohol, the worst of which was that after the first week, no one wanted to be the A. M. As a result of this and one other problem, we have added the following rules:

"The A. M. will receive compensation at the rate of $6.00 per week. The A.M. may delegate her responsibilities to another lodge member in the event that the A.M. is absent from the lodge. The A.M. must compensate the member to whom her duties are delegated, at the rate of $1.00 per day.

"Any member who consumes alcohol on lodge premises must pay a membership surtax of $2.00 per week.

"'Stored' does not necessarily imply overnight. The A.M. must record all alcohol consumed at the lodge, even if consumed the day of purchase."

Three weeks later, the director received a third communication from the Lilac Lodge.

"We have encountered a few additional problems with our rules on alcohol. We have made the following amendments:

"In rule #4, the rate of pay was raised to $12.00 per week. And an additional clause was added in which the A.M. forfeits her compensation if she fails to perform all the requirements.

"In rule #5 the surtax was raised to $4.00 per week. And 'consumes' was changed to 'consumes or stores.' And an additional clause was added clarifying that the surtax

*applies to members who have guests who consume alcohol,
even if the member does not."*

One week later, the director received a fourth communication from the Lilac Lodge.

"Add these amendments:

*"To rule #3.C., add, at the Wednesday meeting only,
(there is too much other business on Mondays and
Fridays.)*

*"To the previous amendment of rule #5, add $4 per
member with guests, not $4.00 per guest."*

Three weeks later, the director received one final communication from the Lilac Lodge.

"All previous rules regarding alcohol repealed. Butt out!"

*"You might think their
dedication to toilets is dumb,
but it's the part I like best."*

Chip Mathias
Vocational Rehabilitation
Counselor

CHAPTER FIFTEEN

TEAM ANGIE

There were seven people waiting for Angie to make a decision.
"Team Angie," Chip called them. There were sometimes as
many as ten members of Team Angie, but the hospital staff and
Angie's "consumer advocate" were not present for this particular
waiting session, otherwise known as a "case conference."

Their wait was doomed to failure. Angie hadn't made a
decision in twenty-nine years and she wasn't about to start now.
Good thing too. The middle of a Team-Angie meeting would
have been a disastrous time and place to make her first. Every
member of Team Angie was pleading with Angie to make a
decision, but that was just protocol. Actually, the very existence
of Team Angie was based on the premise that Angie would not
make a decision.

Her voc-rehab counselor, Chip, was apparently on some
kind of power trip, trying to force Angie to give up her apart-

ment as a strategy to dominate Team-Angie. Carol, Angie's county social worker, was resisting the power play. The understood goal was to move clients out of group homes and into apartments. Angie already had an apartment; she was not facing eviction as half of Carol's clients were. Moving her to a group home didn't make much sense to Carol. Carol sided with the two young apartment trainers, Michael and Allyson, from the Twenty-First Century Program.

"Tasks Unlimited," thought Allyson, "was the perfect name for this awful, nineteenth century kind of program. The staff at Tasks didn't care about these poor helpless people the way she and Michael did. They only cared about cleaning toilets. They should put this program in a museum of discredited treatments, with leeches and lobotomies. It was unthinkable that Angie would transfer to a group home after all the work she and Michael had done to make Angie independent. If Ray, the Tasks Training Coordinator, thought cleaning toilets was such a great thing, he could clean them himself."

The most entertaining element of the meeting so far had been the oneupmanship among Ray, Carol, and Michael around the fantasy of Angie making a decision. Ray had made a first pre-emptive strike with his opening remarks. Team-Angie wasn't warmed up yet, and the reference slipped by without response; only once. From then on, a remark by anyone suggesting that the ultimate decision was up to Angie brought quick, enthusiastic, and increasingly loud agreement from Team Angie, like a southern congregation Amening the pastor's condemnation of a particularly vile sin. Even Angie got into it, "Yeah, she's got to decide." This uncharacteristic reference to herself in the third person troubled Ray, but when questioned, Angie clarified that she understood they were talking about her.

At one point, Michael demanded that Angie make a decision. Angie wasn't the brightest bulb on the tree, but she knew how to handle unreasonable expectations. "Yes, I understand that it's my future we're talking about, so I have to decide. I guess I'll just do what's best."

"Meaning what?" pressed Michael.

"I know you're trying to help me. I screw up sometimes, but I know everybody here has my best interest at heart. So that's what I'll do."

"Not transfer?"

"Right."

"Angie," interjected Ray, "when we talked last week, I thought you agreed that the Lodge Training Program would be a better situation for you."

"It sounds great."

"So you will transfer?"

"Sure!"

"Angie," interjected Allyson, "you don't want to give up your apartment after you've worked so hard to get one?"

"Of course not."

"Do you understand that if you transfer to the Lodge Training Program most of your Social Security and all of your Minnesota Rent Assistance will go to the group home?"

"Yeah."

"So you will lose your apartment because you won't be able to pay the rent."

"Well, maybe my parents could pay the rent on my apartment while I'm in the Lodge Training Program." Carefully avoiding eye contact with her father, Arthur, Angie looked hopefully toward her mother, Jo Anne.

"Angie," said Ray, "the whole point of the Lodge Training Program is to prepare you for the lodge. We talked about this last week. Twenty-First Century is an apartment training program. If you graduate from the Lodge Training Program, you can go to a lodge. You won't need that ratty apartment."

"Oh, that will work out then."

"Her apartment is not ratty," Allyson said in an indignant tone. "At least it's hers."

"Whatever," said Ray. "It's small and cramped and in a crummy neighborhood. Remember how beautiful the Lilac Lodge was when we visited, Angie? How much you liked it and how you said you hoped you could move there when you graduate from LTP?"

"Yeah, it was nice."

"Wait a minute, " screeched Allyson in a voice pitched higher than she intended, "when did you take her to visit a Lodge? You had no right to do that without our approval. You said the purpose of this meeting was to discuss the possibility of Angie transferring to the Lodge Training Program, but you've been sneaking around behind our backs and have her half moved already."

"Not really," said Ray defensively.

"Get this straight," Allyson continued, "Angie has her own apartment, thanks to the Twenty-First Century program, and she's independent. Michael and I have worked hard to keep Angie in this apartment, and she's not going to give it up."

"I have to agree," said Carol, "Keeping Angie in her apartment should be everyone's primary goal."

"Not everybody's," said Chip. "At voc-rehab, our primary goal is getting Angie a job. If she wants an apartment and is capable of maintaining one, great. But it's a secondary goal as far as we're concerned."

"I understand your hands are tied by the federal rules, but you're allowed to use common sense, aren't you?" asked Carol. "You don't want Angie going backwards, from independent living to a group home."

"Not unless there was a clear connection to Angie getting a job."

"Exactly," said Carol. "And how is moving to a group home going to make Angie a better janitor? If Angie hasn't shown any aptitude for janitorial work, what difference does it make where she lives?"

"Janitorial work is demeaning," said Allyson. "No one should have to clean toilets. No wonder ..."

"Gonna be a lot of dirty toilets," interjected Chip.

"... she doesn't show any aptitude?"

"What do they mean by 'aptitude,'" Jo Anne whispered to Arthur.

"What?"

"They keep talking about 'aptitude.' What does it mean?"

"It means she's slow," said Arthur in a whisper louder than most people's regular voices.

"Not slow exactly," said Carol, "it means ... well ... Ray, explain to the Nelsons what you mean when you say that Angie doesn't show aptitude for janitorial work."

"I never said it," said Ray. "She's doing fine, actually; there's no problem with her aptitude."

"Really?" asked Chip. "That's not what you've been telling me."

"I don't mean she's doing great; Angie is struggling like a lot of our trainees do."

"Imagine that," smirked Allyson, "people struggling to work up enthusiasm about cleaning toilets. Maybe they just don't have the same fascination with porcelain that you people seem to have."

"Her enthusiasm is fine; it's her consistency which needs work. And the only thing I'm fascinated with is giving Angie a chance to succeed."

"She succeeded already! She's independent. She doesn't have to clean toilets to be a success."

"Would you knock it off with the toilets already! She does

not even do bathrooms; she's on a trashing route."

"I used to clean bathrooms with Harvey," said Angie. "He taught me how to use the Sparkle Bright and the PT15."

"I have to agree with Allyson," ventured Carol, "whether Angie is cleaning bathrooms or emptying trash, whether she is successful or struggling, whether she has aptitude or not, ... I don't know; I just can't see the backward step of giving up the apartment."

"Backward" used for the second time in the conversation pushed a button Ray couldn't control. "We keep saying 'backward,' but LTP is short-term training, like going to vo-tech or basic training in the army. If Angie could graduate from LTP, she could go to a lodge and ...'"

"Another group home!" exclaimed Michael. Turning to Arthur, "You don't want your daughter to give up her independence, do you Mr. Nelson?"

"... but that's my point," Ray continued. "A Lodge isn't necessarily a backward step, because it would replace Angie's independence with interdependence and ...'"

"Bee Ess!" said Michael.

"Angie is not independent now," said Ray.

"Well, at least she lives independently," said Carol.

"No, she doesn't! Not by any stretch of the imagination."

"She maintains her own apartment," said Michael; "it beats a group home."

"Now, that's bullshit," Ray said, glaring at Michael.

"Ray," asked Chip, "why don't you share what you've told me about Angie's current lifestyle, a day-in-the-life-sort of thing?"

"Is that really necessary?" asked Michael.

"It helped me understand why Ray is recommending the transfer. I don't know if Carol has the whole picture."

"If Angie's story needs telling," said Allyson, "why don't we have Angie tell it in her own words?"

"Actually," said Chip, "I would like to hear Ray tell the entire team the story he told me. Then you and Angie and the Nelsons can tell your side of the story, and we'll all be on the same page."

"Well, okay," began Ray, "typically Michael or Allyson gets Angie out of bed about 9:30."

"We don't even have a key to her apartment," said Allyson.

"She gets up to let you in. Then Allyson makes her breakfast."

"We do it together," said Allyson. "It's part of the training."

"It's a bowl of cereal!" thundered Ray.

"I'm teaching her to put fruit in it so she'll get a few vitamins." Glancing at Michael, looking a little embarrassed, then glaring at Ray, "You've spent four months teaching her how to empty a wastebasket!"

"Toilets!" sneered Ray.

"Look," said Carol, "maybe we should just let Ray tell his little story, and then Allyson can rebut the important points," raising her voice on "important."

"Well," continued Ray, "Allyson fixes Angie's breakfast, and while she eats Allyson writes down what she is supposed to do that day. And while Angie showers Allyson straightens up her apartment ... What I mean is, while Angie showers, Allyson and Angie, together as a training exercise, clean her apartment. On Wednesday, Allyson does Angie's laundry ... I mean they do it together ... as a training exercise."

"Cut it out," said Carol.

"Anyway, Allyson or Michael go over Angie's instructions for the day one more time before they leave, about 11:00. As soon as they're gone, Angie throws the list away and walks three blocks to her parents' house. Jo Anne fixes lunch, and they watch the soaps until 2:30. Arthur, who is semi-retired, working part time at the post office, gets home in time to drive Angie to our job-club meeting. After the meeting, she rides in the van to the job site with the other trainees.

"About 8:30, Trevor, one of our client drivers, drops her off in front of her apartment building. Angie then walks three blocks back to her parents. Our policy requires Trevor to wait until she's inside the building, because winter before last, a trainee slipped on the ice and broke his wrist after the van had driven away. So Angie goes through the lobby door of her building, Trevor drives away, then Angie walks to her parents' house. The three of them have supper and watch a little more TV.

"Arthur goes to bed after the news, but Angie and Jo Anne stay up to watch Carson and then Letterman. Angie loves Letterman."

"He's a funny guy," said Angie.

"About 1:30am, Jo Anne gets Arthur up so he can drive Angie home. Arthur goes into Angie's apartment with her and looks to make sure everything is okay, then he goes home and back to bed. A typical day in the life of Angie Nelson."

"So what's the point?" asked Michael.

"Is it true?" asked Carol.

"It's twisted and exaggerated," said Allyson, "I don't do Angie's laundry, I don't even help her."

"Well, mostly I do it," admitted Jo Anne. "Angie uses too much soap or none at all. I just throw her things in with mine. It's no extra work."

"I can see why you dispute Angie's independence," Carol said to Ray, "but will a lodge be any different?"

"For starters she'll be financially independent. She won't qualify for Minnesota Rent Assistance and there will be no need for Jo Anne to slip her money," Ray said glancing at Jo Anne. He was guessing, but she didn't argue. "Angie will do her own laundry, clean her own room, and share in the grocery shopping and meal preparation."

"Won't the Tasks staff just pick up," Carol continued, "where the Twenty-First Century staff and her parents leave off?"

" It won't be possible. The Lodge Coordinator will be present in the lodge less than Allyson and Michael are present in Angie's apartment now, and will have four or five other people to deal with while she's there."

"It seems," observed Carol, "as though Angie is pretty good at acting helpless and getting other people to do things which she should be doing for herself. What's to keep her from conning the other residents of the lodge into taking care of her?"

"For starters, clients are less easily conned than staff. The lodge members didn't go to college to become 'helping professionals' and they won't get paid to take care of Angie."

"More likely she'll be exploited by the others," said Allyson.

"Sure, she might get exploited in some minor way; we'll try to keep an eye on it. And maybe she will con someone into helping her with her laundry. Maybe both; that's what we call interdependence."

"What's the point?" asked Michael. "Isn't it better for Angie to keep her own apartment with a little help from Allyson and her mom, than to live in a group home where she'll need help from people who have their own problems? Living with a group of people who all have problems sounds like a step backward to me."

"Not at all," continued Ray. "Living with people who have problems is as common as living with other people, which is very common. In her current situation, it seems as though Angie is the problem, which everyone except Angie tries to solve. If she makes it to a Lodge, Angie will still be part of the problem, but she'll be part of the solution too."

"That's all grand," said Carol, "but you said if she graduates to a lodge. How is moving to your residential program going to make her a better janitor?"

"She'll get support for coming to work every day, for one thing," said Ray. "I won't be getting a call twice a week from Allyson saying Angie can't work tonight because she's not feeling well."

"You expect her to work when she's sick?" sneered Allyson. "You call that support?"

Ray asked, "Carol, if I'm not mistaken, you have a cold?"

"Yes"

"But you're working?"

"I wish I wasn't."

"Exacto Mundo!" shouted Ray. "You're not feeling so hot. You should be home in bed. But here you are."

"She is a dedicated professional," argued Allyson. "She is here today despite a slight cold because she has a responsibility to make sure Angie gets a fair deal. You expect Angie to dedicate her life, in sickness or in health, to cleaning toilets?"

"Yes! We're not just talking toilets, but yes, we expect Angie to take her job just as seriously as Carol takes hers."

"That," said Michael, "is the stupidest thing I've heard yet."

"Ha!" said Ray.

Chip cut him off before he could continue, "Since Angie hasn't shown any inclination to make a decision, I will. I ..."

"Now wait a minute," Carol cut Chip off. "Angie doesn't forfeit her right to choose just because she hasn't exercised it quick enough to suit you. You aren't Angie's legal guardian."

"No, I can't make decisions for Angie. But I can make decisions for the State of Minnesota Department of Vocational Rehabilitation. I have decided we are not going to continue funding a voc-rehab program for Angie which her living situation doesn't support."

Michael's scowl turned to a grin, "So you'll hook her up with a different voc provider then?" But the scowl returned as Chip continued.

"No, sorry, I'm afraid not. You think their dedication to toilets is stupid, but it's the part I like best about Tasks. Not the toilets, the dedication. It may sound stupid to expect Angie to develop dedication to cleaning toilets, but that's exactly what she needs.

"Angie, if you are willing to transfer to the Lodge Training Program, the State will continue to fund your vocational rehabilitation a few months more. If you're ready to throw in the towel on ever holding a job and just watch TV the rest of your so-far miserable life, that's okay too. It's your choice!"

"That's not a choice," said Carol. "You can't reduce her options to your favorite program or nothing. She has the right to a real choice."

"Sure, she has rights, and she can appeal my decision if she wants, but it'll be a waste of everyone's time. Tasks is not necessarily my favorite program for all clients in all situations, but it's the fourth one I've funded for Angie, and it will be the last. Most voc-rehab clients only get two chances, and if they screw those up they're S.O.L. There is not enough money to pay for repetitive failure. What about the disabled who aren't getting any services? Don't they have rights?"

"Don't bully us," objected Carol.

"I'm not bullying anybody. If Angie wants to have a job, a fact not in evidence, she can move to LTP. If she wants Twenty-First to keep her in her apartment forever without a job, then fine."

No one spoke right away. "I tend to agree with this direction in one sense," Carol finally said reflectively. "It's obvious that Angie has trouble making decisions. I think we aggravate that by arguing about how good the apartment is, or all this nonsense about toilets. If we don't know the answers, how can Angie? I think you do Angie a favor by reducing the decision to job versus apartment. I don't necessarily accept as fact that Angie can never ever hold a job if she chooses an apartment now; nor do I believe that Angie can never ever have her own apartment if she chooses a job now. But for now it appears Angie has trouble holding a job and trouble performing all the functions required to live independently, so maybe it is a bit unrealistic to think she can handle both at this time."

"So choose, Angie," Chip demanded. "Job or apartment?" Silence.

"Pick one," said Arthur.

"Right now?" asked Angie.

"Now," said Arthur, "make a decision."

"Well," said Angie after a long pause, "I don't know." More silence.

Ray wondered who would crack. He was hoping it would be that bitch Allyson, but it was Carol.

"On second thought, this isn't right. We can't do this to her."

"Do what?" Chip exploded. "Force a twenty-nine-year-old woman to make an adult decision?"

"Ambivalence is part of the illness," Carol explained. "Angie didn't ask to have schizophrenia. We all need to cut her some slack."

"Look," said Chip, somewhat less explosively but still angry, "jobs are for adults; and apartments are for adults. How can you put a woman in a apartment and call her independent if she is incapable of making a basic adult decision?"

"You don't understand the requirement to accommodate under ADA."

"Technically," said Ray, "our job is to help Angie overcome her illness by teaching her how to make decisions, not to indulge her schizophrenia by eliminating the expectation of a decision."

It was the opening Michael had been waiting for. "You can do this, Angie. You can resolve this. Just tell everybody you love your apartment, you love your independence, and you aren't going to give them up for a job you don't even like. You do love your apartment and your independence, don't you Angie?"

"Uh huh."

"Just say it, Angie, 'I want to keep my apartment.'"

"What was it you said a couple of weeks ago?" Arthur suddenly asked Ray, ignoring Michael and Angie. "Something about her mom and me dying off?"

"Oh," said Ray, "I didn't say anything about anybody dying."

" I knew what you meant," said Arthur. "I'm sixty-seven and Jo Anne is sixty-four, and we're not getting any younger. Jo Anne might live a long time yet, but I won't. When I'm gone Jo Anne needs to concentrate on taking care of herself, not Angie and Johnny."

"Who's Johnny?" Chip asked.

When no one answered right away, Carol filled him in, "That's Angie's older brother. He has schizophrenia also."

"He's in Mendota State Hospital," added Jo Anne.

"So what were you saying?" Carol asked Arthur.

"The girl needs a job! Any fool can find an apartment if she can hold a job and earn a living. Even Angie!"

"But what do YOU say, Angie, the apartment or the job?" asked Michael.

"I said she'll choose the job!"

"But she has to decide."

"Tell him, Angie."

"What?"

"Tell him you'll keep the job and give up the apartment."

"Okay."

"The meeting's over," said Arthur.

"Amen," said Chip, as he jumped up to leave.

"This is outrageous," said Michael. Allyson vigorously nodded her agreement.

"I'm going to take Ray's advice," said Carol. They all looked at her. "I'm putting this cold to bed."

Arthur died several years ago and last year Jo Anne moved to a nursing home. Angie went to visit her a couple of times, but she hasn't seen her in over six months. Her brother, Johnny, committed suicide two weeks after his discharge from Mendota State Hospital.

Angie struggled in the Lodge Training Program. Others who entered after she did graduated ahead of her. Ray questioned whether she would ever graduate. Thinking of how difficult the transfer-in conference had been, and dreading a transfer-out conference, he gave Angie a little extra attention and lowered the bar for graduation just slightly. Eventually she was given the nod and was sent to the Lilac Lodge. Chip, Ray, Arthur and Jo Anne, and Carol attended her graduation party. Michael and Allyson were invited but did not attend.

Angie has been at Lilac for nine years now. Other than her hard-earned vacations and the week she broke her wrist ice skating, she hasn't missed a day of work in nine years. At minimum wage, she is the lowest paid member of the Lilac Lodge, but she manages to support herself. It helps that she doesn't smoke or drink. Most of her disposable income goes for videos. She owns every movie Paul Newman or Robert Redford ever made.

"I would like to work full time like the rest of the guys, but I have my wife and son to think about."

Trevor McKinley
Painters Lodge

CHAPTER SIXTEEN

THE IMMACULATE PATERNITY

Trevor met Megan while attending college, he at St. John's, she at nearby St. Ben's. He pledged Phi Iota Sigma, known as the "Fish." Even though St. John's was a Benedictine College, the Fish was the only fraternity with a strong religious focus. The other fraternities at St. John's had nominal rules against drugs, underage drinking, pre-marital sex, lying, cheating on exams, etc., all the things that boys go to college for in the first place. But only the Fish took them seriously. Occasionally a Fish would break a rule, but when he did, it was a big deal; the Fish would agonize over it for days.

Megan had pledged the Fish's St. Ben's counterpart, the "Doves" of Delta Omega Upsilon. The Doves had basically the same set of beliefs and rules as the Fish. Being awash in a sea of sin and debauchery (*i.e.*, college life), the Fish and the Doves were drawn to each other. The school year was full of social events at which the Fish hosted the Doves or the Doves hosted the Fish. Naturally a lot of Fish-Dove dating ensued. A Fish was the only type of boy a Dove could safely date.

Trevor was particularly attracted to a Dove named Connie. She was two inches taller than he, with long black hair she wore in a braid down the middle of her back. She had an enchanting smile. He noticed her right away, at the first social event of their freshman year. Unfortunately, the older Fish noticed also. The first two years, Glen and Tommy, the respective Fish Presidents during Trevor's freshman and sophomore years, filled Connie's social calendar.

Things turned around for Trevor during his junior year. With Glen graduated and Tommy going to school somewhere in Wisconsin, Trevor got up the nerve to ask Connie out. They went to movies in town twice, plus the winter Snowball and the spring Prom. Trevor also went on one other date, and Connie dated several other Fish and at least one Phi Delt that Trevor knew about, but he considered Connie his girl.

Connie seemed to change over the summer. When they came back for their senior year, she was much more worldly. Not only more worldly than Trevor, but also more worldly than most of the other Doves or Fish. She still attended most of the official Dove-Fish social events, but she dated several other St. John's boys as well. She went to Homecoming with the star line-backer from the football team, definitely not a Fish. She was cordial to Trevor at the mixers, but he could never seem to get her alone long enough to ask her where they stood. And she never returned the phone messages he left at Dove House.

Just as Trevor was about to give up hope, Connie agreed to go to Snowball with him; they had a wonderful time. At one point, they were leaving the dance floor when the football star stopped them. He said hello to Trevor, then he asked Connie to dance. Connie asked Trevor if he minded. Trevor said he did.

Connie shrugged at the football player as if to say, "I can't, I'm with him." After he left, she told Trevor she hadn't really wanted to dance with the big jerk anyway.

Twice after Snowball, however, she turned down his movie date invitations. Trevor was puzzled by these rejections, but as the spring of their senior year approached, he was optimistic about his relationship with Connie. He was devastated, therefore, when he asked her to Prom, not so much by her refusal as by her reason: her "boyfriend" was coming up from the Cities.

Trevor didn't know what to say. Connie did. She suggested he take her roommate, Megan. Megan had recently broken up with another Fish and didn't have a date for Prom. Despondent, Trevor agreed.

He had known Megan, also a senior, since they were all freshmen. She was short and blond, kind of perky and really smart. She was slightly overweight but kind of cute. He neither liked nor disliked her. If anything, he was slightly intimidated by her because she had a reputation as a serious scholar, whereas Trevor struggled to get an "A" or "B" in anything other than music.

Trevor and Megan had a nice time at Prom. They went out to dinner first with Trevor's roommate and his girlfriend. Neither Megan nor Trevor was a great dancer, but they danced quite a bit anyway. It was easier than forcing conversation. They knew each other well enough to eliminate an introductory type of conversation, and yet not well enough to discuss anything serious. So they danced and acted shy and did the standard Prom stuff. He made sure they kept their distance from Connie and the "boyfriend." He made no attempt to kiss Megan when he took her home. There was an unwritten rule that Doves didn't kiss Fish until the second date. Trevor took even the unwritten rules seriously, and he assumed that she did too.

He didn't see or talk to Megan for a couple of days after Prom. Then he ran into another Dove, who told him Megan had expected him to call. So he did, and they ended up going to a movie in town. He planned to kiss her at the end of the date, but other people were around and he didn't have the opportunity.

Trevor's third date with Megan was an extraordinary event. It was the Tuesday evening before graduation, right in the middle of finals. He was surprised that Megan, who seemed so serious about academics, would go out during finals week. But it was her idea; she called him and suggested a little Italian restaurant in St. Cloud.

On the way to town, Megan talked about her plans to become a CPA. She was graduating Summa Cum Laude and planned to take graduate courses at the University of Minnesota in the fall. She even had her eye on a particular apartment complex in a fashionable area of St. Paul. Trevor was embarrassed by the informality of his plans; he would be returning to his native Rochester and living with his parents while he looked for a job. Sales probably; he didn't think he could make a living in music unless he taught, which didn't interest him much. During dinner, Megan turned the conversation to weddings. She was very excited that two Dove-Fish couples — Lisa and Larry, Sharon and Bill, were planning summer weddings. She loved the orderliness of it, Doves marrying Fish, right after graduation, starting a new life together. Trevor agreed that it was nice. Not only for Lisa, Larry, Sharon and Bill, but also for all the Doves and Fish who would get to see each other at the weddings. He had been asked to play at Bill's reception. He wondered silently if Connie would attend, and if she would bring the "boyfriend" if she did. He politely told Megan that he looked forward to seeing her at both weddings.

"Let's have our own!" Megan excitedly blurted out.

"What?"

"Let's have our own wedding. The third one of the summer. In August, before my classes start at the University. Wouldn't that be perfect?"

"Sure ... uh ... you and I ... I mean you mean you and I get married?"

"Wouldn't it be great? Lisa and Larry in June, Sharon and Bill in July, Megan and Trevor in August; it's perfect. You do want to get married don't you?"

"Well, sure. I guess I always thought I would get married some day. I just wasn't thinking it would be so soon."

"Well, we could wait until the fall, but August is perfect. Don't you think?"

"Yeah, I guess so."

Megan's discussion of the wedding plans dominated conversation through the rest of dinner and during the drive back to St. Ben's. She gave Trevor a choice between two weekends in August. (As it would turn out, however, the chapel at St. Ben's was booked solid the weekend he chose, so they were stuck with Friday night of the other weekend.)

Many thoughts ran through his head as he slowed the car to a stop in front of Dove House. He had trouble focusing on any one idea. Mostly he felt sick to his stomach. He was considering his need to go into Dove House to use the main floor restroom when Megan leaned over and pecked him on the cheek. He vaguely remembers her saying something about an accounting final the next day.

"See you tomorrow," she said, as she bounded up the walk.

Trevor didn't tell anyone right away; his fraternity brothers heard about it from other Doves. When they asked him about it, he said "uh-huh," and grinned sheepishly.

Graduation came and went very fast. He saw Megan each day, but only briefly and always in the company of other Doves. Their engagement was always the main topic of conversation, whether he was present or not; the Doves were all abuzz. He never got to ask the questions which bothered him.

Questions like, "Why? Why now? Why me? Do you love me? How is it possible that you could love me?" He knew he didn't love her. He didn't know her well enough. He recognized his feelings for Connie, and for a girl named Julie back in high school, as mere infatuations. Surely love had to be more than that; didn't it? What did she see in him? Surely it had to be more than convenience. There must be something about him which she thought was special. Something that would make a bright, level-headed girl like Megan want to do something so impulsive. The depths of her plans were both terrifying and reassuring. How could he have become so deeply involved in a plan so advanced without even knowing about it?

Despite his confusion, he felt a certain confidence in her plan. She seemed to have everything figured out, right to the smallest detail. And the life she described, as much to her friends, in front of Trevor, as directly to him, was not unattractive, especially compared to his vague options in Rochester. She was smarter than he was, and he had always assumed that girls know more about love than boys. So what did he know? Maybe she had it figured out that they would fall in love after the wedding? Maybe that's the way it works? Larry and Bill knew Lisa and Sharon better than he knew Megan, but were even they in love?

In the end he answered his own questions. Megan was a practical girl who seemed to know what she was doing. He trusted her.

His parents were surprised to hear, when he called the night before graduation, that he was marrying a girl he had never mentioned before. And so soon. His mother asked the obvious question. He was both flattered and embarrassed by the question. And he knew, even over the phone, that his mother was embarrassed asking it. He explained they were waiting until after marriage to have sex. He couldn't tell if his mother was relieved or skeptical.

His parents talked it over on the drive up the next morning. It seemed impulsive, but both kids were twenty-two-year-old college graduates, whereas they themselves had been only nineteen when they got married. Their friends would all assume a hasty marriage was a forced marriage, but if Trevor was telling the truth, people would believe it by late winter. Trevor's father had been worried about the dynamics of having a grown son living under his roof, so in some ways he was relieved that Trevor would not be moving home. They were anxious to meet this girl and her parents.

Megan's brother, Dan, had a friend with an apartment in St. Paul, not too far from where Megan would be living, who was looking for a summer roommate. Trevor was startled to learn that Megan had committed him to take the room without talking to him about it, but he had to agree it was a convenient arrangement.

The summer went quickly. He found a temporary job as a security guard while he looked for permanent employment. He had friends working in the Twin Cities as professional musicians, and he got two invitations to audition for part-time gigs: one as part of a thrown-together warm-up act for a popular local group planning a Midwest tour; and one as an accompanist for a theater group. He passed up the former audition because if he had landed the job, the tour would have conflicted with his wedding. He passed up the latter after talking it over with

Megan. The play would have been fun to do and probably he could have found a substitute for the weekend of the wedding, but the security job paid better and Megan stressed the importance of saving money. He had plenty of time to look for a sales position, but his heart wasn't in it. He figured it would be better to wait until after the wedding and the honeymoon in San Diego.

He talked to Megan by phone every day, but she was awfully busy planning the wedding and he was working nights, so they didn't see each other all that often. He wanted to be alone with her, to take her to dinner, to have a "date." Only it seemed weird to ask your fiancée for a date. Megan dismissed his concern, pointing out that they would have a lifetime to spend together after the wedding.

Trevor's buddies held a bachelor party for him the night before the wedding. They met at an apartment in Minneapolis, and then they went to a nearby Irish bar. Everyone kept buying him drinks. He was not an experienced or enthusiastic drinker, but if a man couldn't get drunk his last night as a bachelor, when could he?

He was deathly ill the next day. He wasn't ready when Dan, his best man and soon-to-be brother-in-law came to pick him up for the drive to St. Ben's. Trevor's summer roommate and Dan joked about how much trouble he would be in if he were late for his own wedding, but he was too sick to laugh. He finally got his stuff together and climbed into Dan's car. It was a ninety-minute drive to St. Ben's. He alternated trying to sleep and holding his head out the window for fresh air. Neither helped.

He remembers lifting Megan's veil and kissing her when Father Paul told him to, and realizing it was the first time. Otherwise, being sick is his primary memory of the wedding. He threw up during the reception. He assumes Megan must have been furious with him for being so ill, but he doesn't remember her saying anything about it at the time. They left the reception about 10 p.m. and drove to a motel in Plymouth where Megan had reserved a room. He fell asleep in the car and doesn't remember anything until he woke up the next morning. He was bare chested but still in his tuxedo pants, lying on top of the covers. She was getting dressed.

"You had better get showered and changed," she said, "we need to be at the airport in an hour."

Their wedding day had been a long one, even for Megan, and the day that followed was not much better. They rushed to get to the airport on time, but then their plane was an hour late leaving. They had to change planes in Denver, and when they finally got to San Diego they had to wait a long time for their luggage. They checked into their hotel, had dinner, and watched the sun set. It was only 9 p.m. San Diego time, but it was 11 p.m. Minnesota time. They were both exhausted, and he still didn't feel so good.

As tired and half-sick as he was, Trevor was looking forward to consummating his marriage. He was pretty sure he had not done so in the honeymoon suite in Plymouth. He brushed his teeth and got into bed. He waited impatiently for Megan to come out of the bathroom. She seemed to take forever. He imagined she was preparing, somehow, for the consummation event.

She finally emerged, looking different that he expected. She was wearing a short but plain cotton nightgown. Her blond hair was pinned back away from her face in kind of an odd and unattractive manner. She had removed her lipstick and eye shadow, and covered her entire face with some sort of whitish gunk. (She went on to perform this bedtime routine every night of their weeklong honeymoon, citing the dangers that the San Diego sun and wind posed to a girl's skin.) He was slightly put off by her facial treatment, but the outline of her breasts show-ing through her lightweight nightgown reminded him of his sacred mission.

She seemed to know what he was thinking and spoke before he did. "I know you are anxious to do it, but I haven't quite gotten over last night's debacle. It's a very special thing to me, and I hope it is to you. I think we should wait to try again until we're both completely ready."

Trevor didn't know what to say. All day he had felt her disappointment. Indeed, he was disappointed in himself, and felt very guilty about getting drunk at the bachelor party. But what did "try again" mean, he wondered. He searched his still-throbbing brain for a clue. Had they attempted sex last night? Had he been alert enough to make a clumsy attempt, but too drunk or ill to perform? Before he could think of what to say, Megan plopped down in an armchair, turned on a lamp, and began to read a magazine.

He lay awake trying to remember the previous night, but he drew a blank. He remembered he was still wearing his tuxe-do pants when he woke up, and he thought the fly was zipped. So how hard could they have tried? Unless she put the pants back on him, but why would she have done that? He was tired, his head hurt, and eventually he fell asleep. Megan was still reading.

He was feeling much better the next day. They walked around and did a little shopping in the morning. They were planning to spend the afternoon on the beach. As they finished lunch, Trevor explained how much better he was feeling and how "ready" he felt for the real beginning of their married life. "We could go back to the hotel right now," he suggested. "It's only a few blocks away."

Megan was offended by his suggestion that their marriage would be anymore "real" after they had had sex. "That's a disgusting suggestion. Is sex the only reason you married me?"

"Well no, of course not."

"If you don't have any respect for me, at least you could show a little for our relationship, for the institution of marriage."

"But I was brought up to believe that sex was a healthy thing within a marriage. 'Wait for marriage,' the nuns always said, 'it will be more special.'"

"If you want it to be special, then don't pressure me. I'm not some whore you can have sex with whenever you're in the mood. I'm your wife. Don't you want it to be special for me too? Don't you care if I'm in the mood?"

"Of course I do! But when will that be?"

"I was in the mood, if you must know, on our wedding night. When you threw up all over yourself, it kind of killed the mood for me."

"I told you I was sorry. What can I do to make it up to you? Are we never going to have sex because I messed up the wedding?"

"Of course we are. We agreed to have two kids. Just don't pressure me."

Trevor didn't say anything more about sex for the rest of the week, for fear of pressuring her. But he thought about it plenty. He knew his friends would tease him about it when he got back to St. Paul. He would lie of course. He couldn't very well tell his friends he hadn't "gotten any" on his honeymoon. He knew the basics, but still a virgin, he wondered if he could invent enough plausible detail to tell a convincing story. He considered a story that they had both been terribly ill, near death almost, and had mutually agreed to postpone the consummation.

But a serious attempt at consummation occurred their final night in San Diego. They had a nice dinner, danced a little, and took a moonlight stroll on the beach. When they got back to the hotel, Megan put on a special honeymoon nightgown she had received as a shower present. The nightgown and her nervous smile told him this was the big night.

Trevor felt he should take charge. But his inexperience in such matters and his deepening sense of intimidation held him back. She had grown comfortable with the lead role, throughout their week of marriage, and never considered relinquishing it for sex. So Megan directed the activity. But she was also a virgin, with even less locker-room training than Trevor.

She was prepared for it to hurt, especially the first time. She understood that pain was a necessary, even symbolic, part of the ritual. She accepted, even embraced, the idea of pain as part of her wifely fate, and as a forerunner of the blessed pain of childbirth. Even so, she was apprehensive. The anticipation of pain was her primary emotion as she welcomed Trevor to their marriage bed.

Not raised on a farm and unexposed to pornography, Megan was astonished by the size of Trevor's erect penis. She hadn't intended to look, but the feel of it as she guided it toward her tiny vagina caused her to gasp and throw back the sheet. Growing up, she had occasionally glimpsed her father's and brother's flaccid penises and thought them overly large to accept inside her body. But the object which now protruded from her husband's crotch was fully the size of a banana. She knew that bananas were the source of crude and disgusting humor, but surely her new husband was some sort of anatomical freak. She felt certain any attempt to insert this disgusting and abnormal appendage into her precious vagina would cause serious injury to one of them or the other, if not both. Thus ended their first attempt.

Once settled into married life in St. Paul, Megan had the opportunity to discuss sex with her newly married girlfriends, and also with another friend who had been married two years and was expecting her first child. She was surprised by their attitude change. Before marriage, sex had been a rare and thoroughly embarrassing topic among them, a necessary task associated with marriage. Now, it seemed as though it was all they talked about. Descriptions were general, never graphic, but their references to it were constant. She couldn't tell if they enjoyed the act itself, or simply the thrill of being newly married women who could, for the first time in their lives, admit to having done it. She also came to understand there was nothing abnormal about Trevor's anatomy.

This latter knowledge, and her friends' sense of comfort with the sexual aspect of marriage, led to multiple attempts at consummation. She and Trevor tried more than a dozen times over the first eighteen months of marriage. Trevor achieved external orgasm twice, but full penetration never occurred. Megan couldn't get past the pain, and particularly, the fear of pain. Over time, Trevor accepted the theory that intercourse would inevitably be extremely painful for Megan, and he grew as apprehensive of it as she was. Both were too embarrassed to discuss this problem with anyone else. Even in later years, when they participated in marriage counseling at church, sex was never discussed graphically. They never sought medical advice.

The final blow to the couple's sex-life occurred on a Saturday afternoon, early in the second spring of their marriage. Megan was in a housecleaning mood. It was difficult to find something to clean in their small apartment because she was a fastidious person who cleaned up several times a day, and Trevor was neater than she was. He was obsessive about neatness. Early on, she had ironed and folded a couple of his shirts, only to later find him re-ironing and re-folding the same shirts to get them just right. She never went in his dresser, knowing without looking, that she would find his socks and underwear folded neatly, sorted by color and stacked in perfect rows.

On this Saturday afternoon, however, Trevor was working and she was desperate to clean something. It occurred to her that the shelf paper lining their dresser drawers had not been changed since they were first married. The paper in her dresser was in pretty good shape, but she changed it anyway. Then she started on his dresser. She found a surprise in the bottom of the drawer, underneath neatly folded sweaters.

It was a three-month-old copy of *Playboy Magazine*; a Christmas issue no less. She felt nauseated and staggered to the bathroom where she retched repeatedly. After twenty minutes she returned to the bedroom. The cover, featuring a semi-naked woman in a Santa's Elf costume, and the recognition of the name "Playboy" had been enough to cause her original reaction. When she returned, the magazine was on the floor where she had dropped it, open to the centerfold photo. She could tell that the magazine, and especially the center photo, had been looked at over and over again. There was no mistaking who had done the looking. She felt horribly violated to think that she had married and tried repeatedly to have sex with a man guilty of such perversion as to have studied obscene photos in the sanctity of their bedroom.

She packed up all his things and stacked the boxes just inside the door to their apartment. She put the magazine on top of the pile. When he returned from work she met him at the door. She told him to get out. She never wanted to see him again. He sat down on the floor next to his piled up belongings and cried. He told her how sorry he was, that he never meant to hurt her. He promised never to think about sex again. Eventually she forgave him.

He slept on the couch that night, and for the next couple of nights. On Wednesday, the twin beds she had ordered on Monday were delivered. He carried the almost new queen sized bed to the dumpster. The tension over sex, which had troubled their marriage, was resolved.

Megan was working for a mid-sized accounting firm. She was good at it. When she passed her CPA test, they made her a junior, and later a full partner.

Trevor failed at a long series of sales jobs. He jammed with his musical friends on Sunday afternoons and had several invitations over the years to join working bands, but Megan didn't approve of the late hours professional musicians kept. He filled in for a band at a local bar sometimes, but she would insist that he take his clothes off, wash them and shower in the laundry room of their building before entering their apartment because he smelled so badly of cigarette smoke. She kept urging him to get a teaching certificate so he could teach music at a high school. He refused because teenagers made him nervous. Eventually he landed a fairly steady job selling Buicks. He didn't make much money because it was strictly commission and he rarely closed a sale. But the owner of the dealership seemed to like him, and it was something to do. Besides, Megan made enough money that the two of them lived pretty well, eventually moving to a very expensive apartment in the suburb of Edina.

Although the sex question was resolved to Megan's satisfaction, she still wanted children. She would even have endured the pain and humiliation of sex with Trevor if she could be certain to get pregnant. But she knew that pregnancy would likely require repeated intercourse, with no guarantees. She had a better idea.

She convinced Trevor they should adopt. They applied to the Catholic adoption agency. They were perfect candidates: young, healthy, employed, stable. The only problem was a shortage of healthy white babies. They talked it over and quickly agreed. Healthy was important to them, white wasn't. Eighteen months later, in their eighth year of marriage, they adopted Jerome, a healthy six-week old boy of mixed race.

They seemed the perfect family for a while.

Jerome was more expensive, however, than they expected. The adoption fees had wiped out their savings, and the cost of baby food, diapers, and child care was eating up their budget. Megan's accounting firm had lost key clients and the partners had agreed to tighten their belts.

Since Trevor rarely actually sold a Buick, she suggested he quit his job and take care of Jerome full time. As little as he was making, they would come out ahead financially. Trevor loved little Jerome, but he hated changing diapers, and he couldn't see himself as a stay-at-home dad.

She also suggested he cut back on his favorite entertainment, which was drinking with friends and co-workers. He especially liked bars with live music. Megan continued to work long hours, socialized with her accounting friends, and all the rest of her time was spent with Jerome. Since the adoption, Trevor felt like a third wheel. More and more it became his habit to stop for a drink after work. Soon the only exceptions were Monday and Wednesday nights when he played basketball with some guys from high school, and went drinking with them instead. Friends or co-workers, one drink usually turned into three or four. Often, he found himself buying more rounds than his share, just to keep the party going. He understood and agreed with Megan's advice to cut back his spending habits, and he fully intended to; it just never happened.

The rising cost of living continued to surprise them. Out of diapers and on to Big Wheels, Jerome was more expensive than ever, and not as completely healthy as they had hoped. They had interpreted the adoption agency's description of "normal" health as meaning "perfect" health, but no guarantees were attached. Jerome was physically robust and active, but a little slow in his emotional development. This became more obvious after he entered a formal pre-school program at age three. (Years later, Jerome would have been quickly diagnosed with Fetal-Alcohol-Syndrome, but FAS was not widely recognized in the early eighties.) The teacher said that Jerome didn't understand sharing, and didn't seem to develop relationships with his peers. She recommended special programs and private schooling.

Megan and Trevor had intended all along to provide Jerome with a Catholic education like the ones they had both enjoyed. They were shocked, however, when they sat down with Sister Gwen to discuss the cost. A year of half-day kindergarten cost $2,100. First grade was going to cost $3,800, and probably a little more each succeeding year as the parish struggled to keep up with inflation. There was, Sister Gwen explained, noticing their sticker shock, a sliding fee scale to accommodate the less fortunate children in the parish, and to ensure diversity in the classroom. Somewhat stunned and humiliated to think of themselves as charity cases, they provided the necessary financial data, only to learn that their original instincts had been correct; they weren't eligible for a discount. Sister Gwen explained the option of having the Parish Scholarship Committee review any special financial hardships they might want to bring to the Committee's attention. Megan quickly announced that it wouldn't be necessary. They would simply tighten their belts.

Megan did tighten her belt, and she pressured Trevor to tighten his. She put him on an allowance. She challenged him to find a better job; selling something people actually wanted to buy, for example. She started challenging his behavior every time he came home smelling of alcohol. In response, he went to bars less often, but when he went, he drank more. Their arguments became louder and more vicious. She accused him of being an alcoholic. He denied it. She challenged him to get evaluated to find out. He refused.

Midway through Jerome's first-grade year, Megan's accounting practice dissolved. The partners were not getting along and their revenue base was shrinking rather than growing. Two of the partners pulled out, taking all the best customers with them. It took Megan only a week to find another job, working in a large firm. She was earning only slightly less, but now no longer a partner, she had little optimism about her financial future. She studied her budget and decided to eliminate her main problem.

Trevor had a difficult time accepting the reality of the divorce papers. Despite the non-sexual nature of their relationship, he had grown to love Megan, and he thought she loved him. His first thought was that she was just using the divorce papers to get his attention; and she certainly had it. Although he had never admitted it to her, he wondered himself if maybe he was an alcoholic after all. He decided to seek professional evaluation to appease Megan. He even made up his mind to accept treatment if they said he needed it. And if the evaluation was negative, Megan would have to accept that his drinking was within normal limits. Either way, they would be reconciled.

He was greatly surprised by the results of his evaluation. He was not chemically dependent, they said, he was manic-depressive and obsessive-compulsive. There were some medications he could take. They might help, and they might not.

In the meantime, he attempted to continue living with Megan and Jerome. He understood she was mad at him, but as they had basically separate lives, what difference did it make? She had the locks changed, but he tricked the security guard into giving him a key. She told the security guard not to let Trevor into the building, but the security system was mostly for appearances; it wasn't that hard for Trevor to slip by. Three weeks after being served with divorce papers, he had still made no effort to find other living quarters. Megan got a restraining order.

The restraining order meant even less to Trevor than the divorce papers had. He still believed in the inevitability of a reconciliation. He gave not the slightest thought to the legal implications of the court order. Half an hour after he returned home that evening, the police arrived and arrested him. He spent the night in jail and went to court the next day. He does not remember any discussion of mental illness during his court appearance; he certainly didn't mention his recent diagnosis, and he hadn't told Megan about it so they couldn't have learned about it from her. But for reasons unknown to Trevor, the judge ordered a psychiatric evaluation. The results were the same as when he was evaluated for chemical dependency; his real problem was manic-depression and obsessive compulsive disorder.

He spent two weeks in Fairfield Hospital. When he got out, he went straight to his favorite bar. It was mid-afternoon, no music or anything. He drank alone for the first and only time of his life. When he got good and drunk, he went "home" to Megan's. He really had nowhere else to go. They had lectured him at the hospital about not going to see Megan, but nobody had helped him make any other arrangements. His son and his clothes were still there.

The security guard made a minimal effort to stop him, and then called to warn Megan. The locks had been changed again, and this time he couldn't get into the apartment. He was still pounding on the door and screaming when the police came. He spent forty-eight hours in a detox center in Minneapolis, and then six more weeks in Fairfield.

As the date of his second discharge approached, a social worker suggested a halfway house. Trevor insisted he wanted to go home. The social worker explained what would happen if he tried. He was still optimistic about reconciliation. He didn't think Megan could be serious about going through with the divorce. He was anxious to talk to her, to share his newfound insight into his illness. The social worker pointed out that Megan had neither visited during his six-week hospitalization nor returned his calls. He argued that Megan had never really liked hospitals, and she didn't understand his diagnosis. Besides, he pointed out, less than half of his fellow patients on the psychiatric ward got visitors. That didn't mean they couldn't go home.

He ended up at the Tasks Unlimited Lodge Training Program. Darcy, the social worker there, kept telling him the same thing: he couldn't go home. Darcy said she could help him find an apartment if he didn't want to go to a lodge. But Trevor had never lived alone in his life; the thought of it seemed kind of scary. He asked Dick, a bachelor from the Buick dealership, if he could share his two-bedroom apartment in Roseville. The gist of Dick's lengthy excuse was "no." So Trevor agreed to go to the Painters Lodge until the inevitable reconciliation with Megan.

A few months after he moved into the lodge he got papers in the mail indicating that his civil divorce was final and ordering him to pay child support. He didn't mind paying the child support as he was making better money working for Tasks as a janitor than he had made some months at the car lot. It didn't make any sense to him, however, that Megan would push this divorce thing so far. Would they have to have a civil marriage ceremony after the reconciliation, even though they were still married in the eyes of the church? The needless expense of it all was so uncharacteristic of Megan. What was she thinking of? He made up his mind right then that things were going to be different between them from then on.

He decided he needed to be more assertive: more of an Old Testament kind of husband and father, making decisions and sticking to them. He felt guilty for being so passive during the first thirteen years of their marriage, forcing Megan to make decisions he should have been making. He also felt guilty about the drinking. During his so-called "treatment," he had said what he had to say to please the counselors running the groups, but he hadn't believed any of it. Only now did he realize the real impact of his drinking. His irresponsibility and drunkenness had forced Megan to assume the lead role in their marriage. That was what she was trying to tell him with these divorce papers, "Sober up and take charge of your family." He rushed "home" to explain it to Megan.

Phil, one of his new friends at the Painters, bailed him out of jail. He realized, after the fact, that the police were just doing their job. They didn't understand what Megan was doing. The big question was when would Megan let up? Surely she saw that he was completely sober. Didn't she understand that he had gotten the message about taking charge? Maybe he hadn't explained it clearly. Next time, as soon as the new restraining order expired, he would get it right.

Three years after he moved into the Painters Lodge, after two failed attempts at reconciliation, Trevor received notice of a proposed annulment. He was devastated. He had never taken the civil divorce seriously. It had less significance to him than the Social Security papers he had filled out claiming to be psychiatrically disabled. That was a hoax too, but at least it provided an income supplement and health insurance for Jerome. An annulment, however, was a serious threat to his family.

He contested the annulment. A hearing was held before a panel of a priest and two lay counselors who would make a joint recommendation to the bishop. Trevor testified that he loved Megan and always had. He had been faithful to her even during their three-year separation. He explained his developing understanding of the husband's role as spiritual leader of the family. His trump card was that they had been married now for sixteen years. Annulments were for teenagers. How could the church even consider annulling a sixteen-year marriage begun in the chapel at St. Ben's?

Megan argued that they had both been young and foolish when they got married. Furthermore, she hadn't known Trevor was mentally unfit. Her trump card was stronger than his was. Although they had been civilly married for thirteen years, the marriage had never been consummated. When questioned, Trevor admitted that this was true.

Although it was six weeks before either was notified of the outcome, the panel was quick and unanimous in their decision. Trevor was devastated by the results. He had trouble accepting that the Church, to which he had been so faithful, would do this to him. Also surprising were the extreme actions Megan had taken to make her point. For a while, after the annulment, he considered the possibility that their relationship might really be over. Or, as the Church seemed to be saying, it had never existed in the first place. His doubts surfaced again two years later when he heard a rumor that Megan had married the head of her accounting firm and was pregnant.

But mostly he is able to put such negative thoughts out of his mind. He knows Megan will be true to their vows, regardless of the rumors or what the bishop decided. He is confident that soon she will realize that their separation has gone on too long, and will call to tell him to come home.

In the meantime it is important to maintain his disability so that Medicaid will pay for the special school Jerome attends. That's why he can't work full time as many lodge members are now doing. That would tick Megan off, which might delay their reconciliation.

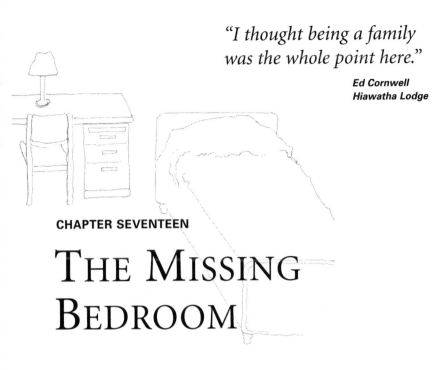

*"I thought being a family
was the whole point here."*

Ed Cornwell
Hiawatha Lodge

CHAPTER SEVENTEEN

THE MISSING
BEDROOM

Hiawatha Lodge was moving. It was too late to argue about that.

This did not prevent Ed and Dale from arguing with each other. But two guys who had argued for years on the subject of who had been the youngest governor in Minnesota history were not about to let relevance get in their way. On occasion, other Hiawathans had suggested going to the library to resolve the youngest governor or the thousand other things that Ed and Dale argued about, but nobody ever did, least of all Ed or Dale.

The Hiawathans were moving to the suburbs, 7701 Blaisdell, to be exact. This too, was beyond argument. Except for Ed and Dale.

"It's about time Hiawatha moves, all the other lodges have upgraded," said Ed

"Why should we move just because everybody else does?"

asked Dale. "That's a stupid reason to move."

"Come on, this house is a dump."

"I like this house."

"You're the only one," said Ed.

"I'm the only one who thinks it through."

"Thinks WHAT through?"

"Thinks through the implications of us moving to the 'burbs. What have we been talking about?" asked Dale.

"Well, I admit that that's the downside. We should stay in the city."

"That's ridiculous. There is no point in moving at all unless we move to the 'burbs.

"Why would we want to move to the 'burbs?" asked Ed.

"To get out of this neighborhood. That's why we're moving."

"There are plenty of nice neighborhoods in the city."

"Name one," demanded Dale.

They went on and on like that for weeks.

But that was history. Ten months ago the Hiawathans had voted (five to one) to move. They did so knowing full well that they would almost surely end up in the suburbs, as the mortgage subsidies to which Tasks had access applied only to the suburbs. Now that Tasks had bought them a house, a nice house on 77th and Blaisdell, right across from a park and only two blocks from a strip mall with stores that sold just about everything the Hiawathans could ever use, they couldn't very well say, "No."

So that was it. They were moving. To the suburbs. On June first, give or take a day. All the Hiawathans were going. No one could stay behind, not even Dale, because Gentry Lodge, the lodge that did construction instead of janitorial, was going to rehab the old Hiawatha Lodge. It would take months and the building would be uninhabitable for much of that time. And no one knew who would live there after; Tasks might even sell it.

So all six had to move. That was the problem.

Someone at Tasks, no one was admitting responsibility, had bought Hiawatha Lodge a house with five bedrooms. (7701 Blaisdell had been a three-bedroom plus living room, dining room, kitchen, two baths, a den and a garage. A previous owner had finished the walk-out basement into a fourth bedroom, a third bath, and a beautiful large family room. Tasks had immediately converted the den to a bedroom and added a deck.) With five bedrooms, three baths, a large dining room, two living areas and a brand new deck, 7701 Blaisdell offered deluxe accommodations for a five-member lodge. But there were six human Hiawathans, plus Lovey the cat.

The old house, from which Hiawatha was moving, had only four bedrooms and one bath, so they were accustomed to sharing space. But a private bedroom for everyone was part of the dream, part of why they voted to move.

"They probably just miscounted," said Jan.

"Yeah, they always think Ed and I are the same person," said Ed's roommate and brother, Everett.

"Now they want one of us to switch lodges," said Ed. "I don't get it. In the lodge training program they told me that lodges are suppose to be like families."

"We are a family," said Jan. "The Hiawathans are the only family I got."

"I never heard," Ed continued, "of a family kicking out one of its members so that they could move to a smaller house."

"I wouldn't mind if Ed or Dale switched," Marsha confessed when neither Ed or Dale was around. "If they wanted to, I mean. I wouldn't mind not hearing the two of them argue all day long."

"Yeah, they're a pain in the ass," said Lois. "But they're Hiawathans and the pain is Hiawatha pain. It would be like giving another lodge our dirty laundry."

As June first drew closer, Tasks stepped up its efforts to entice one of the Hiawathans to choose another lodge. The Bay Lodge, with a little encouragement from Tasks management, invited the Hiawathans over for coffee and Shirley's homemade brownies. The understood purpose was to pitch the empty bedroom at Bay Lodge as the solution to everyone's problem. The Hiawathans went out of courtesy to the Bays, not to mention that Shirley's brownies were legendary. But no one bit on the empty room.

With two weeks to go before the move, room assignments had to be settled. It was increasingly obvious that two of the Hiawathans would have to share a room, presumably the original master bedroom with the walk-in closet. But who?

No one had any intention of rooming with Dale, and Marsha had staked an early claim to the converted den. On the other hand, Jan and Lois had shared a room at Hiawatha Lodge for years, as had Ed and Everett. All four were comfortable with their partners, so maintaining one of the existing pairs was the obvious solution. They all wanted a private room, but none of them wanted to argue too strenuously for a single room at the risk of offending their long-time roommate and friend. There had been several meetings on the subject, each sounding like a tape recording of the one before.

"I guess Lois and I could share a room," said Jan.

"Yeah, sure," said Lois.

"Well, Ed and I are brothers, after all," said Everett. "We don't mind sharing."

"No, no, you don't have to do that," said Lois. "I kind of like that master bedroom with the southern exposure. Jan and I would do fine there."

"You know," said Ed, "Ev and I have a lot less stuff than you and Jan. We would have no problem getting all of our stuff in the one closet."

"Well, it's a bigger room and a bigger closet than what we've got now. We would be fine in there," said Jan.

The conversation went on and on in this vein until one day Ed suggested, "We could convert the family room into a sixth bedroom."

"That's dumb," said Dale. "Where would we put the big TV?"

"We could put it in the living room."

"Where would we entertain guests when someone is watching TV?" Dale demanded to know.

"When was the last time you had a guest?"

"I have guests! Other people have guests."

"Well," Ed continued, "what if we made two bedrooms out of the family room? We could put the T.V. in one of the downstairs bedrooms and call it a den."

"That's dumber yet."

"It's big enough for two bedrooms."

"How would you get to the north bedroom?"

"You could go through the other room?"

"You can't do that. You want me walking through your bedroom?"

"There's an outside door."

"Did you ever hear of winter?"

"Well, they could build a hallway or something," Ed offered. But he could tell from the collective body language that the Hiawathans were siding with Dale on this one.

"I would really prefer to room with Lois," said Jan on the eve of the big move. I would prefer that to my own room. You don't mind, do you Lois?"

"No, that'll be fine," said Lois.

"Maybe you should only pay half rent," suggested Ed.

"There are five bedrooms, so we should divide the rent five ways, and you two each pay a half share."

"That's dumb," said Dale. "They won't eat half as much groceries just because they're sharing a room."

"The two of them together don't eat as much as you do. We should charge you double for groceries."

"The rent goes directly to Tasks Unlimited for the mortgage and stuff," explained Marsha, the Hiawatha Treasurer. "The rent has nothing to do with our grocery money."

"Well, they'll use just as much of the mortgage as everybody else," argued Dale.

"It's okay," said Jan, "we can pay full rent."

"How about three-quarters?" suggested Everett.

"Where is the rest going to come from?" demanded Dale.

"The rest of us will pay a little more," explained Everett.

"If the rest of us pay one-fifth and they pay three-quarters, now there will be too much rent," insisted Dale.

"I think I can work out the math," said Marsha.

And she did. And the Hiawathans moved to 7701 Blaisdell and lived happily ever after.

Especially Ed and Dale, who sit on the deck and argue about the youngest governor.

> *"Haven't you noticed, they*
> *never find any of those kids*
> *on the milk cartons?"*
>
> **Larry Runnich**
> *Painters Lodge*

CHAPTER EIGHTEEN

THE REINCARNATION
OF LARRY

Larry accepts his schizophrenia. He figures his fate should be much worse, given some of the horrible things he has done. He has been a bad person: not in this life actually, but previously.

In one of his previous lives, he was merely exploitive; a rich landowner, cheating his sharecropping tenants, leading a life of opulence and excess while others suffered and died from malnutrition, their suffering aggravated by his efforts to squeeze out every penny.

But in two of his previous lives, he was worse. He was evil incarnate. He slaughtered and tortured people.

In the first of these especially evil lives, he was a captain in the Spanish Inquisition. His squadron provided the muscle for a pair of friars, whose job was to execute or baptize any and all Moors in what had recently become Castilian territory. Father Santiago was sincerely interested in converting the heathens, thus saving their souls from eternity in a fiery hell. Father Burgesso's strategy was to execute as many Moors as possible, and let Satan and St. Peter sort it out. It was all the same to Larry.

But even this was not Larry's most evil history. In a yet more evil life, Larry worked for the KGB, where he and his colleagues were in charge of extracting information from suspected counter-revolutionaries. Many were accused on trumped-up charges and therefore possessed no useful information. Larry sensed this, but he tortured them anyway.

The current Larry, living in the Twin Cities at the dawn of the third millennium, recognizes murder and torture, even exploitation for profit, as wrong. He has no current desire to do any of these things. He can't explain why he did such things in previous lives. Maybe he didn't know right from wrong at the time; maybe he was just an evil person. Either way, he has much to atone for.

He worries about his next life, which could be a lot worse, and could begin any day. The latter fact is especially troubling. He remembers more than a dozen previous lives in considerable detail. He remembers the names of friends and family, in some cases, casual acquaintances. He remembers the dates of significant life events and sometimes the weather. He remembers certain parts of some of his previous lives more clearly than he remembers corresponding events from his current life as Larry Runnich of the Painters Lodge.

But he doesn't remember ever dying. He doesn't remember getting really old, seriously ill, shot (except once in the leg), or hit by a bus. He remembers living, followed by a fuzzy period, from which he doesn't remember anything, followed by memories of being a small boy in his next life. He thinks maybe he died, and went to hell or purgatory or wherever, and just doesn't remember any of it. But his favorite theory is that he has never died yet; when he does finally die, that will be the end of it, no more reincarnation. He thinks that what typically happens is that you get "zapped" from one life right into the next. The fuzzy part he can't quite remember is probably the time spent in the womb, and perhaps infancy.

Larry explains away the common belief in death as the natural endpoint of life in the following way: animals die all the time because animals don't get reincarnated; after a certain number of lives (maybe fixed, maybe variable) people actually die, an event which attracts a lot of attention because it is a big deal; more often, people get zapped out of one life and into the next, but nobody observes this because it happens only when no one is looking. Random disappearances are common, but nobody cares much unless you are a kid, in which case they put your picture on a milk carton.

"You'll notice," Larry points out, "they never find those kids. They don't even bother to look for adults."

Larry lives in fear of being zapped into a much worse life than the current one. He is aware of other theories about reincarnation, whether it really exists and how it works. But one thing for certain, Larry has been zapped at least a couple of times.

By his mother's account, he was perfectly normal until age four-teen and had lots of friends. (A closer look, however, shows that his friends were all three to four years younger than he. He did not get along too well with kids his own age.) He loved baseball. He collected baseball cards. He memorized the statistics. He lived and died with the Minnesota Twins, who played at Met Stadium just a short distance from his house. He not only knew everything about the current Twins, he even followed the fortunes of the Twins' farm teams, and the prospects who might become Twins. He attended as many games as he could. When he couldn't attend, he would lie on his bed with the window open, listening to the play-by-play on the radio, and hearing the roar of the crowd live.

He loved playing baseball almost as much as watching and talking about it. He loved the rituals of spitting, rubbing dirt on the bat, pounding his glove. He loved the strategy and the little tricks, like pick-off plays and double steals. The only problem was, he wasn't good at it. He ran fast enough and was good with the glove, but he had a weak throwing arm and he couldn't get the bat around against kids his own age. Against average kids maybe, but not against the biggest and strongest kids who did most of the Little League pitching. He knew more about baseball than his peers and wasn't shy about telling them so, but they weren't interested in the opinions of a kid who never made the team.

The younger kids were more easily impressed. They looked up to him for his knowledge of the game, and he could hit against them. He was ineligible by age for the Little League teams his friends played on, but they played ten innings of sandlot ball for every inning of Little League, which was mostly about coaches yelling and two hours of infield practice before each game. Some days, he and his young friends would play four on four, or five on five, from 9 in the morning until 9 at night, and he would instruct them along the way on the subtleties of the game.

Then he got zapped for the first time.

It coincided with his starting high school. When he attended the sixth, seventh, and eighth grades at Sacred Heart, his friends, though considerably younger, attended the same school. Their age difference was not a great barrier.

But there was no Catholic boy's high school in
Bloomington. He could have gone to Benilde or St. Thomas, or
even downtown to De LaSalle. His parents chose Prairie
Cathedral. Only two other boys from his eighth grade class at
Sacred Heart enrolled at Prairie Cathedral, and they were close
friends with each other. They didn't think much of Larry.
Worse yet, classes at Prairie Cathedral didn't let out until 3:45,
and then it took an hour bus ride to get home. The neighbor-
hood ball game was almost over by then as dinnertime and
September dusk were approaching.

Even on weekends, he no longer had much in common
with the younger kids, and they frequently left him out.

Larry's mother recounts a major personality change about
this time. "Up until then, he was a normal, happy kid.
Outgoing even. Then suddenly he was morose and brooding.
He wouldn't say a word unless you spoke to him directly. And
then you were lucky to get a 'yes' or a 'no' out of him. He stayed
in his room all the time, stayed in bed if you let him. He was
like a whole different person."

Larry, himself, has very little memory of high school. He
remembers events from his boyhood days at Sacred Heart in
great detail, but his four years at Prairie Cathedral are like a fog.
He remembers not having any friends, and being frightened of
the boys he went to school with. He doesn't remember why. He
doesn't remember being beaten up or teased; mostly the other
kids ignored him.

His mother remembers one incident in which Father
Mackey called to report that Larry had been hiding under a desk
during a history class. Apparently he had been scheduled to
present an oral report about the Civil War, and responded by
slipping under the desk when his turn came. After coaxing
failed, the teacher and several other boys dragged him out. The
teacher took him to the office where he declined to explain his

behavior and curled up into a fetal position. He seemed okay the next day. Larry doesn't remember any of this.

He remembers that during his senior year he got a job as a carry-out at a local grocery store. He liked working better than going to school. After graduation, he got a second job as a cook.

He continued to live with his parents. He was still very, very quiet; "Like a vegetable," his mother says. Between the two jobs, he worked forty to fifty hours a week. He didn't have a car and paid no rent. He spent all his money on heavy metal records and baseball souvenirs.

He received no treatment for mental illness during this time, but even so, a very dramatic change occurred. Larry reports that it happened one day while he was reading the lyrics of a song off a Metallica album. He is not sure if the incident was a near reincarnation which was aborted for some reason, or if his illness was cured by James Hetfield.

His mother can't explain it either, but she agrees it was an amazing transformation. "For five or six years he was this sulking, withdrawn kid, kind of like a vegetable, completely incapable of a conversation. And then one day, boom! He started talking a mile a minute. You couldn't slow him down or get a word in edgewise. Everybody noticed the difference. It was like having our son back after all these years. We thought he got hit in the head or something."

"I think I was partially zapped," says Larry.

The new Larry was not entirely normal either. He couldn't sit still. He couldn't stop talking. He took a third job working the night shift as an attendant at a gas station. Between the three jobs, he was working seventy to eighty hours a week.

This didn't leave much time for sleeping, but he couldn't sleep anyway. He remembers quite vividly that he would lie down only two or three times a week, and sleep only an hour or two at a time, often less. His sister suspected he was taking some sort of speed, but Larry insists he never did. "I never took any drugs. I hate 'em. I'll drink a beer once in a while at a Twins game, but I don't even like alcohol. I never took street drugs."

Regardless, it was during this manic period that he first began to remember his previous lives. The memories came to him in waves, with more and more clarity and detail, over a two-year period. Some of the memories were pleasant. But the memories of himself as a cruel landlord, a zealous executioner, and a sadistic torturer freaked him out.

This was part of the reason he didn't sleep much. He could remember bits and pieces of his previous lives even while working, but they were especially vivid if he tried to lie down in a quiet room. Even the mild or pleasant memories confused him. Sometimes, waking up in a dark, quiet room, he couldn't remember which life was real, which life he was in now.

The memories of evil deeds done in the past lives were especially frightening. In addition to his growing recognition of the inevitable atonement waiting for him in future lives, he became concerned that someone would try to get even with him in this life. Most of his non-working hours were spent out and about in the community; it was better than being alone with his memories. And being a big talker, he was constantly meeting new people. The problem was, he lived in fear of being recognized by someone from a previous life, especially someone he had tortured.

He knew that people didn't look exactly the same from one life to the next; sometimes they had more hair or less hair or different color hair. But he felt he looked pretty much the same as he had during his evil lives, especially around the eyes. He studied the eyes of every new person he met, to see if he recognized one of his former victims. He felt it was critical that he recognize them before they recognized him. He cut his hair real short and bleached it blond, but he didn't trust that that would be enough. The fear that someone would track him down and kill him in his sleep contributed to his sleeplessness.

Over time, his paranoia increased. This, plus his efforts to explain his theory of reincarnation to his parents, caused them to take him to see the family doctor. The doctor referred Larry to a psychiatrist who placed him in a local hospital. It was the first of what would become six community psychiatric hospitalizations. Larry did not like being locked up. He especially did not like the fact that they would take his belt and wallet on admission. "I was never suicidal and there is nothing to buy in the psych ward. I don't know why they treat people like that."

The treatment would generally include tranquilizers, which provided him with some much needed sleep, and some sort of anti-psychotic medication. Larry doesn't remember the anti-psychotic medications having much effect on him.

"They didn't really change the way I thought about stuff. But I didn't like being there, so I would deny knowledge of my previous lives and tell the nurses I no longer believed in reincarnation. I couldn't go back to my parents unless my psychiatrist said it was okay; and I didn't have anywhere else to go. I would have told them whatever it took to get out of the hospital. When I look back at it, I am ashamed of myself for lying. But when they put you in a place like that, you feel like getting out is the most important thing in the world. I haven't been back to the hospital in all the time I've been at the Painters Lodge, but I might lie my way out again if I had to."

During Larry's sixth hospitalization, his third during 1982, he was shipped off to Mendota State Hospital. The doctor at Mendota put him on Trilafon and Lithium. He had been on both before, but not at the same time. He doesn't remember the combination initially being any more effective than other anti-psychotic therapies.

At Mendota he got involved in a program to train people to live in Fairweather Lodges. The part he liked best about it was they taught people how to do janitorial work. Until then, his favorite kind of work was anything which allowed him to talk to people while he worked. At first, janitorial didn't seem so good for that. It was hard to conduct a conversation with anybody when he was always on the move. Later on, they taught him how to run a low-speed buffer.

He absolutely fell in love with the low-speed buffer.

Nowadays, high-speed buffers are used to shine a floor. They spin a fine pad over a floor at four to six thousand rpms. Anybody can run one. But a low-speed spins a coarse pad at five to seven hundred rpms. Low-speeds don't float, they grind. It takes skill to run a low-speed. If you don't know what you are doing, a low-speed will get away from you: break table legs, punch a hole in a wall, even climb a wall if the wall doesn't cave. Low-speeds and coarse pads are used for stripping dirty wax and for smoothing out a fresh coat, a common process back when Larry was learning the trade.

At first, the low-speed leaped out of his hands every time he engaged the clutch. He thought it was trying to kill him. Over time, he learned to control a low-speed. The trick was learning that control comes from balance, not strength. (No one is strong enough to overpower an unbalanced buffer.) They told him all this before he ever got his hands on one, but being told how to control a low-speed is like being told how to ride a bike. You have to get a feel for it. Half the guys in the Fairweather Program at Mendota never did learn how to control one.

Larry became an artist. If you set a full glass of water on a waxed floor, Larry could strip the wax all the way around, leaving a circle of wax a half inch in diameter larger than the water glass, and never spill a drop. The janitorial instructor at Mendota said Larry could "make a low-speed buffer whistle

Dixie." Larry thought operating a low-speed buffer was the best job in the world.

Larry jumped at the opportunity to join the Painters Lodge. They promised him he could run a low-speed every night if he wanted. He also liked the idea of living with other people who had been in the hospital themselves. They didn't seem as though they would be as quick to send him back to the hospital as his parents always were.

When he arrived at the lodge early in 1983, his belief in reincarnation was unshaken. He also remembers being afraid of everything, including the other Painters. Dr. Bob kept tinkering with his meds. In mid-1984, Dr. Bob made yet another adjustment, slightly raising both the Trilafon and the Lithium. Within days, Larry's paranoia and general anxiety disappeared.

"It was almost like being zapped," says Larry. "One day I was afraid of everybody and everything, and the next day I was not afraid of anything."

Larry never attended a high school baseball game while he was at Prairie Cathedral. He attended a game a couple of years later when two of his young friends were playing for Benilde. This was during his silent, withdrawn period, so he doesn't remember anything about the game except that he went.

He must have enjoyed it, because the next spring, following his aborted-zapping or Metallica-induced cure, he attended every Benilde home game. His two friends shared first base, depending on who had been hitting lately. But Tony also had a younger brother, Ricky, a sophomore pitcher, on the team.

Sophomore pitchers rarely get to pitch in high school varsity games, but young Ricky had an extraordinary arm. By the end of the season, he was the team's hardest thrower and guttiest pitcher. Larry followed Benilde the next two seasons to see if

Ricky could get control of his curveball (he did) and master a slider (he did not).

By the time Larry joined the Painters Lodge, his interest in professional baseball had waned, and he had developed a real passion for high school baseball. His improved mental health gave him the courage to attend games played on fields other than Benilde's, even if it meant riding several buses to get there and back. His janitorial wages financed these excursions, and the organized routine of his life, influenced by the structure of the lodge, helped him in planning his schedule.

At first he went only to Benilde games, first home, then both home and away, then a few Prairie Cathedral games even when they weren't playing Benilde. Then he got interested in some of the other teams they played, public schools as well as private, and some of the players on the other teams. Larry would take an interest in a certain player whose team was playing Benilde, and go to see his next game against some other team. Then that team would have an upcoming game against one of the top-rated teams in the state, and Larry would want to see that. He would follow these teams as they advanced through the playoffs toward the state championships.

As the years went by, Larry figured out where to get complete advance schedules from all the major Twin City high school conferences. He would study them in March, writing the dates on his calendar when the big games were scheduled between conference contenders, and agonizing for weeks over which of two key match-ups scheduled on the same day he would attend.

He became a well-recognized figure at high school baseball games. His old friend Tony (Ricky the pitcher's older brother) went with him to a few games each year, but Tony had a nine-to-five job, so mostly Larry went alone.

The new Larry was a very sociable and talkative kind of

guy. Over time, he got friendly with some of the coaches, a few of the college and professional scouts, and a lot of the umpires. Tony noticed, whenever he went with him, that most of the umps seemed to know Larry, and some would even talk to him through the backstop while the pitchers were warming up between innings. He and the umps would chat about games the ump had worked earlier in the season and who the best players were. It was Tony who suggested that Larry become an umpire. Larry dismissed the idea at first; he had no training as an umpire, and the State High School League would never hire a "crazy person" as an ump. Tony wasn't so sure; Larry loved the game, he knew all the rules, he had good eyesight and pretty good judgment in most areas. Tony called up the State High School League and found out that all Larry would have to do would be to interview, produce two character references (Tony would be one), and pass a test on baseball rules. Tony also learned that they were mildly desperate for umpires; it didn't pay very well and most people weren't available mid-afternoon. Most of the existing umpires were older guys who had umped for years, and were constantly threatening to retire.

"You don't have to tell them you're crazy," Tony advised. "Don't mention that you live in a group home, and don't bring up that reincarnation stuff."

Larry applied, followed Tony's advice in the interview, and was hired. The first two seasons he mostly worked the bases, teaming with an experienced home plate umpire. By his third season, he was alternating behind the plate. There was quite a bit of turn-over during his third and fourth year, and by his fifth year as a high-school umpire, he found himself as one of the senior members of the umpiring pool. There were a couple of old guys who had umped for thirty years and thousands of games, but with one hundred and fifteen games under his belt, Larry was in the top ten percent of the working umps.

And fairly popular. There were a few coaches here and
there who held grudges against him for missed calls. Larry
admitted that he missed a couple of calls now and then; every
ump did. But most of the coaches liked him. He was an
adequate ump with a consistent strike zone. They liked the fact
that he was often available when someone else cancelled on
short notice, and that he was willing to let a game continue
through a little rain, especially late in the season when schedul-
ing makeup games was difficult. Some coaches objected to his
running conversations with catchers and batters; they wanted
their players to concentrate. But all the coaches appreciated his
love for the game. They might get angry with him temporarily
when a close call went against them, but it was hard to stay
angry with a guy who loved the game as much as he did. After
years of attending high school baseball championships as an
enthusiastic fan, Larry was chosen to ump some of the tournament games. He has now worked more than a dozen state
tournament games, but the first one he worked, Robbinsdale
versus Richfield in the 1991 quarterfinals, was the greatest thrill
of his lifetime.

His friend Tony also turned Larry on to golf. Not watching golf,
playing it. Tony and Ricky had been turned on to golf by a
buddy of Ricky's and sometimes they needed a fourth. Larry
said "no" the first several times Tony asked him, but Tony
persisted and finally he agreed to give it a try. Within two years,
Larry was as passionate about golf as he was about low-speed
buffing and high-school baseball.

Tony was available to play only on weekends, and then only
eighteen holes per weekend because he was raising kids. Larry's
interests quickly outgrew eighteen holes per week. Other than
the Painters, none of whom golfed, Larry didn't have too many

real friends other than Tony. But this did not deter him.

There was a Minneapolis municipal course only four blocks from the Painters Lodge. With a $180 per season resident pass, Larry could play an unlimited number of holes for $6 per weekday. Once the high school baseball season ended, he would play Monday through Friday. And he would get his money's worth, usually playing twenty-seven holes.

Over time, and after a determined effort to promote the sport, he got a few of the Painters interested in golf. None of them were as obsessed with it as Larry, but Trevor would play with him once a week, and Alan and Calvin would play once in a while.

With help from the Tasks Unlimited Recreation Coordinator, Larry organized an annual Tasks Unlimited Golf Tournament each September. Three or four staff would play, plus ten or twelve guys from various lodges. Larry would make up the teams. Basically, whichever team had Chris from the Spirit Lodge always won. Chris played only once a year, and somewhat under duress even then, but he had learned the game as a kid and shot in the eighties, far better than anyone else. Larry never cared if he won or lost; he was just happy to have company around the course.

Along with reincarnation theory, low-speed buffing, high school baseball, and golf, Larry has one other love. Her name is Linda. Unfortunately, she is his best friend's wife, and the mother of his kids.

She and Tony were practically engaged already when Larry first met her. And she was married and pregnant with their son Michael by the time Larry realized he was in love with her. So it was too late. Tony is his best friend, so Larry never speaks openly of his feelings for Linda, but he figures she probably knows.

He sometimes fantasizes about what might have happened if he had met Linda first. Or what might happen if Tony got "zapped" into the next life someday, "Would he step in to be a husband to Linda and a father to Tony's kids?" Mostly he fantasizes about meeting up with Linda in a future life, and marrying her before Tony gets in the way. But then he remembers how evil he was in the past, and concludes that all three of these scenarios are pretty unlikely.

Although he has no real family of his own and even his parents have moved to Arizona, he feels as if he has two families: The Painters and Tony's.

The Painters are great guys and Tony is like a brother to him. He would do anything for a fellow Painter, and they would do anything for him. Tony's kids call him Uncle.

Larry still believes in reincarnation and in the evil of his past lives. He still expects to get "zapped" some day. But until then, life is beautiful: good job, nice place to live, baseball, golf, and family. It worries him a lot because he knows he is really in for it in his next life.

*"You need more staff
in the lodge so that
you can teach people
how to be independent."*

**James Figlicht
Department of Mental Health**

CHAPTER NINETEEN

THAT'S
RESIDENTIAL

The Asylum Movement swept the country in the 1920's.
Asylum, the Latin word for "safe place," was a compassionate
strategy for protecting our most vulnerable citizens from the
dangers of modern life.

By the 50's, Thorazine, the first psychotropic wonder-drug,
became widely used. Thorazine seemed to actually cure some
people, and it moderated the symptoms of almost everyone who
took it. Thanks to Thorazine, the word "discharge" entered the
vocabulary of psychiatric care.

Several researchers advanced the theory that people with
mental illness were better off, *i.e.,* more likely to recover, living
in the community than in the asylum. The researchers reported
their findings to the administrators, who dutifully reported
them to the legislators. All across the country, state legislatures
responded with a collective ho-hum.

Then someone clever added the comment, "and it would be cheaper;" and the great deinstitutionalization was under way. The asylum movement went into reverse, and between 1950 and 1970, asylum (a.k.a. state hospital) populations were reduced by eighty to ninety percent.

The community was not exactly prepared to deal with this. Furthermore, although researchers proposed that the money used to operate the state hospitals "follow the patients into The Community," it never happened. Clever hospital administrators and public employee unions teamed up to maintain staffing levels. While the state hospital populations were falling by almost ninety percent, employee rolls were reduced by less than ten percent. In some states they actually increased. Schizophrenics were given a thirty-day supply of Thorazine and sent to the streets to fend for themselves.

They had to live somewhere. In Minneapolis, as in other cities across the country, a network of "boarding homes" emerged to handle the load. Funding for room and board came mostly through mechanisms designed for the non-disabled indigent; it was minimal and profit margins at the boarding homes were thin. Much to everyone's surprise, conditions were deplorable and the boarding home operators put little of their own money into developing therapeutic milieus.

Reformers demanded change. In Minnesota, the legislature passed a law requiring that any building providing overnight shelter to three or more persons with mental illness be licensed as a "Residential Treatment Facility" and held to certain standards for providing treatment. Although it was years before adequate funding was allocated to provide community treatment, the state began to drive the hated boarding homes out of business. By 1980, the largest boarding homes were razed without providing alternative housing for the tenants, many of whom became homeless, and the medium-sized homes were converted to treatment facilities, driving out another portion of the tenants who preferred homelessness to treatment.

Once it found momentum, the licensing bureaucracy was hard to stop. Lodges operated by Tasks Unlimited had not been the subject of any newspaper articles chronicling abuse of the mentally ill and were presumably not the primary targets of the licensing legislation. They were not, therefore, at the top of the state's hit list. Eventually, however, Lodges were informed in writing that they would need to obtain a license and meet sixteen pages of licensing standards, or shut down.

The Diamonds took the news hard. The legendary Diamond Lodge had been created as the first Tasks lodge and the world's first Fairweather lodge where everyone worked full time. They considered themselves ex-mental patients, and were not accustomed to taking orders from outsiders. Disinclined to disband, they asked their Lodge Coordinator, Francis, for assistance in understanding the often obtuse regulations. All the lodges were affected and Tasks was pondering a system-wide response, but the Diamonds were inclined to handle the matter themselves.

"We've got to take control of our own destiny," said Dean, always quick with a sports cliché.

Every single regulation, dozens of them per page, seemed to rankle the Diamonds. Things like menus being posted seven days in advance, and food prepared to exact specifications so that the licensing inspector could verify that basic nutritional needs were being met, were particularly irritating.

"I ain't cooking from a damn recipe," announced Carl, who fancied himself a bit of a gourmet cook.

The largest, most obvious, problem was a requirement for twenty-four hour, seven-day-a-week staffing. Francis assured the Diamonds that this meant exactly what it sounded like.

He, or someone like him, would need to be physically present in the lodge at all times. (Tasks, for its part, was concerned about the cost of such a service, skeptical that the potential state funding would be sufficient. But cost was the least of the Diamonds' concerns.)

"What do you mean, 'like you?'" Silas asked Francis.

"I'm not going to be here 24-7," he explained, "I've got a life, you know."

"You mean we'll have two Lodge Coordinators?"

"More likely four," said Francis.

"Oh", "shit", or worse, everyone groaned.

Alan immediately jumped to an obscure problem. "How in the Sam Hill are we gonna keep 'em busy?"

This was not exactly the first concern on the minds of most Diamonds, but Francis understood Alan's point. If there were four of him (actually, more like sixteen of him since currently he was present at the Diamonds Lodge only about ten hours per week), the consulting/facilitating role that he played would not be enough to occupy staff's attention for all that time. Inevitably they would become supervisors, or worse yet, therapists.

"I suppose," continued Alan, attempting to answer his own question, "there would be security advantages to having someone here while we're all asleep. As long as they're quiet and don't keep us awake. What will they do overnight?"

"They'll probably wake each of us up a couple of times every night to record our dreams," speculated Phil.

"They wouldn't really do that, would they?" Alan asked, looking at Francis.

"I don't know what the state will require. But in some ways I think Phil is on the right track. You guys are in for analysis."

More groans. This time one "Shit!" and several saltier terms expressing disgust.

They batted the staffing question around for over an hour, an extraordinarily long meeting by Diamond standards, occasionally drifting into side issues.

"What is this stuff about 'V.A.'s?' That just applies to veterans, right?" asked Dean.

"Wrong," explained Francis. "In this case, 'V.A.' stands for 'Vulnerable Adult.' Everyone living in a licensed residential treatment facility is automatically classified as a 'Vulnerable Adult.' And 'Vulnerable Adults,'" Francis continued, anticipating the obvious question, "are protected from 'abuse and neglect.'"

"What does that mean?" asked Alan.

"'Neglect' is when your girlfriend won't have sex with you anymore," suggested Phil.

"Well, kind of," said Francis. "And 'abuse' is when she does have sex with you."

"What do you mean?" asked Silas, who understood abuse to mean having sex by himself.

"'Vulnerable Adults' are considered, like fifteen-year-olds, incompetent to consent to sex. So technically, if the Diamond Lodge was a licensed facility, your girlfriends would be abusing a 'Vulnerable Adult' if they had sex with you, because you were incompetent to consent. It's kind of like statutory rape."

"You gotta be kidding," said Dean.

"Well, I don't know if they would actually prosecute your girlfriends for taking advantage of you guys, but, technically, I guess they could. A more likely scenario would be if your girlfriend was also in a licensed facility." Francis was now looking directly at Phil, who was known to be quite friendly with Gloria from Lilac Lodge, "You could be prosecuted for 'abusing' her."

"Bullshit!" said Phil.

"I'm not saying they would; I'm just saying they could."

"You're saying if Phil has sex with Gloria that's 'abuse;' and if he doesn't that's 'neglect?'"

"Well, that was Phil's definition of 'neglect.' Basically, anything bad that happens to a Vulnerable Adult is 'abuse;' and anything good which doesn't happen is 'neglect.'"

"I've been abused and neglected all my life," observed Alan. "I never knew it was a crime."

At subsequent meetings, several other troubling aspects of the licensing standards were discussed. "They're trying to suck us back into the system," said Phil. "I'm through with the system! I did 25 years in Shakopee and I'm done with it. I busted my hump to get into the Painters, and I busted my hump to make it at the Diamonds. I don't know about you guys, but I'm not going back into the mental health system."

Warren's tone was different, but his sentiments were similar. "You know," he said, "sometimes at family gatherings my brother and my brother-in-law get to talking about the market, and all their investments, and I know they both make ten times as much as I do, and I get to feeling bad about being a janitor.

"But then I get to thinking, 'So what if Stuart is a big-shot actuary? So what if Irv is a dentist? Janitors are just as important as actuaries and dentists, even if the actuaries and dentists don't know it. What would Stuart's fancy-schmantcy office look like if no one dusted, or vacuumed, or took out the trash? Like hell; that's what. No one would want to work there. And what would happen to Irv's practice if he didn't have a good janitorial service to keep the place clean? His patients would get infected with each other's germs; that's what. Janitors are like aesthetic engineers, guardians of the environment. Without good janitors, the United States would look like a third-world country.' At least that's what I tell myself. And then I don't feel so bad about being a janitor.

"And we usually get together at my brother's, or at Julie and Irv's home, both of which are big beautiful houses, and I get to thinking, 'What am I doing living in a group home? I'm forty-

one years old and I'm living with four other guys. All of whom
have mental problems. And one eleven-by-fourteen room is all
I have to call my own.'

"But then I get to thinking, 'The Diamond Lodge is a
beautiful house and Carl has done a beautiful job decorating
it. Besides, I really like these guys. I wouldn't want to live by
myself. I'd go crazy for real. And how much private space do
I really need? I got my own bed, my own desk, my own TV,
a walk-in closet.' I share a bathroom with Dean, but he leaves
my stuff alone and I leave his alone. I saw a thing on TV about
office workers in Tokyo. During the week they sleep in these
little compartments that are like coffins. They only get to go
home on weekends. And even then I'll bet they don't have as
much space to themselves as I do. And people in third-world
countries, how do you suppose they live? And then I don't feel
so bad about living in a group home. I could do worse than
the Diamond Lodge.

"But what I don't like, what I can't get over feeling bad
about, is being in a program. And no offense, Francis, but
you're the person, the thing, that constantly reminds me I'm in
a program. Phil says he feels out of the mental health system
since he came to the Diamonds, but I only feel like that on
weekends, overnight, and when we're working. Every time you
walk in that door, I feel like I'm back in the system. It isn't just
those stupid goal plans we have to do twice a year, or you looking over our bank statement once a month to make sure I'm
keeping the Diamonds' accounts balanced (I don't mind that, I
really don't). But every time I see your face, it's a reminder that
someone doesn't trust me to plan my own affairs and do my
own job. It's not about you personally, but when you're not here
I feel like the Diamond Lodge is my home, our home. As soon
as you walk in, I feel like this is your house, Tasks' facility, part
of the mental health system. We need less staff, not more.'"

"You're preaching to the choir," said Francis. "I'm not the one who says you guys need more staff."

One evening at work, not long after Warren's big speech, Francis asked Alan, the Lodge Chairman, to call a special meeting during breaktime. He had urgent business which couldn't wait until the next afternoon. Francis had just come from the Tasks office where he had heard a rumor. The rumor was that someone at Tasks had talked the licensing enforcement people at the state into visiting a lodge before issuing citations. Just one lodge was all they would have time for.

"Which lodge?" asked Dean.

"That's just it," said Francis. "Tasks hasn't decided yet. I think they're going to decide tomorrow."

"Should be the Diamonds," said Alan.

"No doubt about it," said Phil.

"I thought you guys would say that," said Francis. "I'll call Tasks first thing tomorrow morning."

"Don't ask them;" said Phil, "tell them it's gotta be the Diamonds."

The people from the state included Ms. Dorothy Hansen and her boss, Mr. James Figlicht from the Mental Health Division of the Department of Human Services, and a sinister looking fellow named Johnson from Licensing Enforcement. No first name, no smiling introduction, just "Johnson;" not a big talker, this Johnson. The director of Tasks Unlimited was also present.

Alan led a two-minute "tour;" it was just a house, not much to see, really. Then the director invited the state people to sit down at the dining room table where the Diamonds held their lodge meetings. The Diamonds scrambled for the remaining chairs, and those who didn't get one lurked in the archway.

"Why do we need a license?" Carl asked immediately.

"Oh," Ms. Hansen cleared her throat in a very odd sort of way, "You mean the rule 36 license for Residential Treatment Facilities?"

"We don't want to become a treatment facility," said Warren. "We've already been through 'treatment.'"

"Oh, it doesn't exactly mean that," said Ms. Hansen. "And it's not exactly an optional designation that you ..."

She was interrupted by Warren. "If the word 'treatment' in the phrase 'Residential Treatment Facility' doesn't exactly mean treatment, then what does the word 'Treatment' mean, ex ... ex ... ex" (Warren tended to stutter when he was angry) "exactly? We're all curious, you kn ... kn ... know, exactly."

"Oh," said Ms. Hansen, starting to feel slightly flustered, "I don't know that I can give you precise definitions word by word. The term 'Residential Treatment Facility' is defined explicitly in the state statutes, but I don't have a copy with me."

"Wouldn't an explicit uner ... uner ... uner,"

"Oh," Ms. Hansen cut him off much to everyone's relief, "I think you have the wrong idea here. Licensing won't be a bad thing. The purpose of the licensing is to make your lives better."

"We don't want to be better," suggested Alan.

"We couldn't stand it," added Phil.

"How would it ... it ... it?" stuttered Warren.

"Oh, I can see that you're all quite happy here, in which case the new rules won't make much difference at all. The point of licensing is for everyone across the state to enjoy the same satisfaction that you already have."

"So we don't have to get licensed then?" asked Dean.

"Oh, technically you do. But it doesn't have to change anything. It doesn't mean you're going into treatment. Besides, there is a waiver procedure. If a particular portion of the rule doesn't seem to apply to your unique situation, you can apply for a waiver of that portion."

"I presume," said the director of Tasks, "that those are the one-year waivers. We would need to reapply for each waiver for each lodge every year?"

"Oh, sure," Ms. Hansen felt a sense of relief that the director had entered the conversation. She was uncomfortable discussing complex policy issues directly with the participants and their overly-personalized perspective. "But I don't think it will be as difficult as you make it sound."

"You'll waive the staffing req ... req ... req?" asked Warren.

Ms. Hansen smiled knowingly and looked at the Tasks Director for help. Much to her dismay, he was staring intently out the window as though something fascinating was happening across the street.

She glanced quickly at her boss. He was looking right at her with that passive expression which she knew from experience meant, "This is your problem. I don't like to get involved in this sort of detail." She glanced back at Warren, who was still struggling to finish his sentence, and clenching his teeth so hard that a huge vein running from the hinge of his jaw up one temple and most of the way across his forehead, was throbbing like a flashing neon sign.

"Which part of the staffing requirements?" she inquired.

"The whole thing," said Dean.

"Oh, we can't exactly waive the entire staffing requirements and leave you with no staffing at all," she said trying to make a joke. When no one laughed she felt herself getting flustered again.

"The less sta ... sta ... sta."

"Surely you need some staffing. You said you didn't think your lodges needed twenty-four hour staffing," Hansen said to the side of the director's head, thinking she could force him to answer by asking a direct question. "But I forget, how much staffing do you provide now?"

"Francis is here a couple of hours a day," said Dean. "But only on work days. He's not here at all on the weekends."

She felt her sense of panic growing as she gave up on the Tasks director's profile and turned back toward Dean. "And who is here when she's not?"

"He," said Dean, "Francis is a he."

"We told him it was a girl's name, but he won't change it," added Phil.

"Anyway," Dean continued, "He's it. Francis is the only staff we got."

"Only staff we nee ... nee ... nee," Warren added.

"And you're telling me he is only here a couple of hours a day, five days a week," Ms. Hansen said with a tone of disapproval, staring again at the side of the director's head.

"More like four days," Dean corrected. "He doesn't show up every day."

"Oh look, I don't know why I," (she glared at the director as she emphasized the "I,") "need to explain this to you. But people with mental illness need a certain amount of help in re-adjusting to the community. Someday, with the right staff support, you can graduate from here and get your own apartment, but you're going to need help to reach that level. This very conversation shows your need for help. You seem to be in some collective state of denial."

"How is 'residential' defined?" asked Phil.

"I already explained that I didn't bring those definitions with me. But the definition of 'residential' is pretty obvious, isn't it? You sleep here. You reside here. That's residential."

"So if my girlfriend sleeps over sometimes, that makes her a Vulnerable Adult too?" Phil asked, drawing a giggle from Dean.

"Oh see, that's how twisted this conversation is becoming. Your girlfriend doesn't become a Vulnerable Adult just by walking through that door."

"Not even if she stays over night?"

"No, I don't think so."

"So we can sleep together and there is no 'abuse' on either side?"

"Oh now you're getting into the fine points of the Vulnerable Adults statute. And this isn't the time or place to get into personal matters. You need staff here to give you advice on such matters."

"Francis knows we sleep together. He says you're going to make it illegal," Phil said in a firm and slightly threatening tone.

Ms. Hansen began to cry softly. "Oh, I'm not trying to do anything except explain the law to you. I didn't make the law."

"Then explain to me what the definition of 'residential' is. I'll sleep in the damn garage before I'll become a Vulnerable Adult."

"Oh, it isn't just sleeping," Ms. Hansen sobbed, "it's living, eating. Everyone knows what 'residential' means."

"Then we'll barbecue and eat on the deck!" Phil shouted, "all winter if we have to."

"That's enough!" Mr. Figlicht said. It wasn't clear if he had finally joined in out of male instinct to protect Ms. Hansen, whether he was embarrassed by her crying, or whether he simply had another appointment. "It's pretty clear that we need more staffing in this facility to help you achieve independence."

"Why don't you and I step outside for a moment," Phil said to Figlicht, "and we'll find out which one of us is the Vulnerable Adult."

The Tasks director asked Phil to tone it down a little bit, but it seemed too late to avoid the damage as Ms. Hansen and Mr. Figlicht got up from the table and started to leave. But Just-Johnson, the licensing man who had ridden with them to the Diamond Lodge, didn't move. Instead he cleared his throat as if to speak for the first time.

"It doesn't seem to me that this is the type of facility to which the licensing standards would easily apply."

"Selective enforcement is not within your purview," Ms. Hansen reminded him. "This is a residential mental health facility, and they need a license to stay in business."

"Ah, but is it?" asked Johnson. "You know as well as I do that the statute does not define 'residential' or 'treatment' because those terms are considered obvious and everyone agrees on what they mean. But Mr. Phil here refuses to agree what common words mean, and I believe he is fully prepared to sleep in the garage and cook in the yard to thwart our licensing enforcement."

"Surely you are not going to let that stop you?"

"Obviously our definition would eventually prevail in court, but then Mr. Phil and Mr. Warren will come up with some other cockamamie argument. Quite frankly, my office doesn't have the manpower to fool with it."

"I can't believe you're caving in to this lunacy."

"Honestly, Ms. Hansen, I fail to see what is to be gained by requiring these people to provide more staff. Look at this house. It's a lot nicer than most of the Residential Treatment Facilities we do license."

Figlicht jumped in, "Can't you see they need more staff here if these people are ever going to achieve independence?"

"You say they need more staff, but it looks to me like they're getting along fine. I don't want to assign one of my staff to spend the next three years of his or her life fighting with these people to bring this place down to our standards. I think we should be moving the other programs in this direction."

"You don't know what you're talking about," said Ms. Hansen.

"Let's finish this discussion in the car," said Mr. Figlicht, "I've got an appointment in St. Paul in five minutes."

The Diamonds weren't quite certain what to make of all this, but the director from Tasks said it was a good sign that Just-Johnson winked at him on the way out. When thirty days went by and he hadn't heard anything from licensing or the Mental Health Division, the director got nervous and sent them both a letter saying that Tasks would be happy to apply for a Fairweather Lodge license and offering to help draft the requirements for same.

Almost a year went by. Neither Tasks, nor the Diamonds, nor any of the other lodges heard anything from anybody at the state. Finally, Tasks received a letter from Just-Johnson, whose first named turned out to be Geoffrey.

It was a short letter. It said, "Fairweather Lodge Licenses are not being issued at this time."

APPENDIX I
Facts about Tasks Unlimited

These stories only begin to portray how lodges can improve the lives of people with serious mental illness. The teamwork, the mutual caring, the pride in being a contributing member of society, sets lodge members apart from most "mental health consumers." (Lodge members disdain this term, by the way; they prefer to be known as janitors, drivers, sheetrockers, etc. Their identity emerges from what they produce, not what they consume.)

I expect that for readers unfamiliar with the model, and especially for readers unfamiliar with group homes and serious mental illness, the stories of lodge life will have raised many questions. I have functioned as a spokesperson for Tasks Unlimited and the lodge model long enough to anticipate some of these questions, and I will attempt to answer them here.

Q: *How did Tasks Unlimited get started?*
A: Tasks was created in 1970 by staff from Minnesota's Anoka State Hospital with the assistance of the National Institute of Mental Health's Fairweather Lodge Dissemination Project.

Q: *How has the demand for lodges changed over time?*
A: Tasks Lodges grew quickly during the early seventies, as state hospitals were dramatically downsized. The population of lodges stabilized during the eighties as Tasks and other providers focused on services for people living in individual apartments.

The program experienced another growth spurt in the nineties, fueled by dissatisfaction with the isolation of individual apartments, and a commitment to smaller lodges in upscale neighborhoods. By the year 2000, Tasks was sponsoring sixteen lodges and scrambling to open two more to meet demand.

Figure 1: Lodge growth at Tasks Unlimited

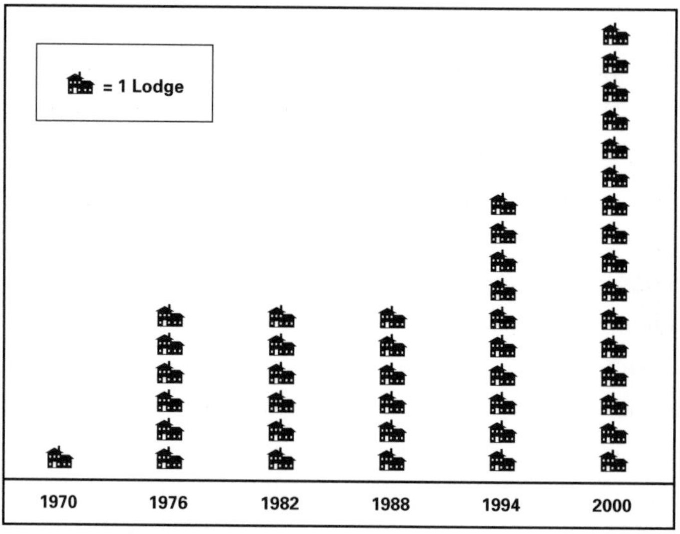

Q: *Does Tasks keep track of long-term outcomes for people entering the lodges?*
A: Beginning in 1990, we have tracked key variables, including days of hospitalization, rates of employment, gross earnings, and type of living situation, for everyone graduating from our Lodge Training Program. We track everyone for five years regardless of whether they choose to stay in a lodge or not.

Q: *What do the data show?*
A: In all categories, there was tremendous improvement compared to their status prior to entry into the Lodge Training Program. Statistically, their standard of living, their social status, even their sense of control over their own lives was

dramatically higher than it was before, and this change is relatively permanent.

As shown in Figure 2, for example, hospitalization dropped from an average of 66 days during the 12 months prior to entry to almost zero after joining.

ONE MIGHT SAY THAT GRADUATING FROM TASKS LODGE TRAINING PROGRAM COMPARES TO GRADUATING FROM COLLEGE AS A SUCCESS-ENHANCING EXPERIENCE.

Figure 2: Average number of days in hospital for people graduating from Tasks Unlimited Lodge Training Program

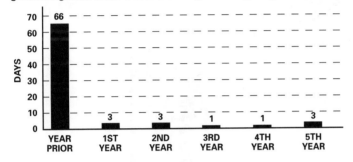

As shown in Figure 3, employment status increased from 16% immediately prior to entry to Tasks to approximately 90% measured on annual anniversaries (of first entering a lodge).

Figure 3: Percentage employed at follow-up

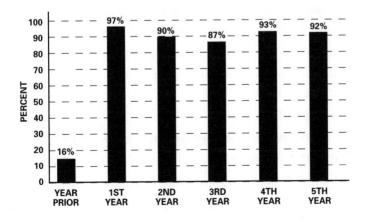

And as shown in Figure 4, residential life immediately prior to entering Tasks was dominated by high dependency situations such as hospitals, treatment programs, etc., compared to highly independent situations (lodges and individual apartments) after five years.

Figure 4: Change in living situation

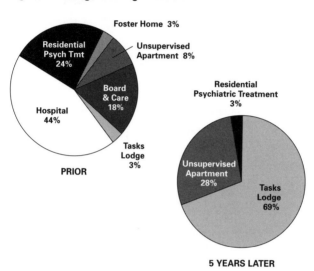

Q: *If Tasks values long-term outcomes, why measure for only 5 years?*
A: Five years seems adequate to establish a pattern. Success rates drop slightly from year one to year two, and after that they stabilize. Informally, I notice that people don't change much during the second five years. Data collection is ongoing, but this is being published in 2000, so 1995 is the most recent year for which the five-year outcome data is available.

Q: *How many people are included in your data? And what is the response rate on follow-ups?*
A: Our data include 62 people, and the response rate for most questions was around 90%.

Q: *The outcome data seem phenomenal; Tasks' admission screening must be highly selective?*
A: We reject fewer than 25% of our applicants. There may be some self-screening going on in the sense that we describe the lodge as a life-changing experience and not everyone is ready to change.

THE DATA ON LODGE TRAINING GRADUATES PRIOR TO ENTRY (66 days in the hospital during the past year, 16% employed) ARE CLOSE TO MOST ESTIMATES OF THE NATIONAL AVERAGES FOR PEOPLE WITH SERIOUS MENTAL ILLNESS.

Q: *What about earnings?*
A: Figure 5 shows average total earnings during the year prior to a person's admission versus average 1998 earnings for lodge members. (The bar at right in Figure 5 represents the 1999 Minnesota state average for disabled workers in individual job placements.)

Figure 5: Earned income prior to lodge vs. 1998

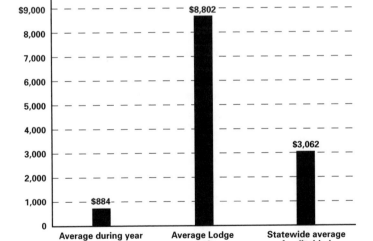

Average during year prior to admit 1990-1997	Average Lodge member 1998	Statewide average for disabled workers
$884	$8,802	$3,062

Q: *What role do taxpayers play in supporting a lodge?*
A: People with serious mental illnesses tend to revolve through cycles of hospitalization, halfway houses, residential treatment, day treatment, intensive case management, subsidized apartments, food stamps, and disability payments; often followed by expensive court proceedings leading to recommitment to the hospital. Not infrequently,

> IT IS NOT UNUSUAL FOR A SINGLE PERSON WITH MENTAL ILLNESS TO COST THE TAXPAYERS $100,000 A YEAR.

these court proceedings are triggered by interventions by police officers, firefighters, or paramedics. No one knows the real cost of all these services, but they aren't cheap.

The Tasks lodge program costs the taxpayers very little, maybe $4,000 per person per year, everything (room and board, supported housing, supported employment, case management, transportation, etc.) included. As shown in Figure 6, the public subsidy to Tasks Unlimited Building Services (TUBS) barely exceeds the payroll tax paid by TUBS. Tasks generally receives less than $3,000 per person per year in public subsidies for the mental health services provided to lodge members. Except for HUD-subsidized mortgages on some of our lodges, lodge members pay the full cost of their own room and board out of their wages.

Figure 6: TUBS payroll vs. taxes paid vs. subsidy received, 1998

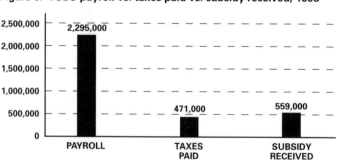

Q: *In the story "Full Time Guys," Silas and others make a conscious decision to forfeit their eligibility for Social Security Disability by working full time. Is that common?*
A: Nationally, it is very uncommon. The Social Security Administration reports that only one-half of 1% of people approved for disability on the grounds of psychiatric difficulties ever return to full time work.

> BY THE YEAR 2000, 38% OF LODGE MEMBERS WERE WORKING FULL TIME.

Q: *Why do lodge members have to work as janitors?*
A: First, let me point out that janitorial work is underrated by people unfamiliar with it. But lodge members don't have to work as janitors, they have choices like everybody else. Several of our current lodge members have jobs outside of Tasks. Other lodge programs around the country are engaged in a variety of businesses including landscaping, furniture refinishing, catering, printing, etc. At Tasks, people can choose between janitorial, mail handling, or our construction company, Rehab Squared; and even within our janitorial business there are a variety of jobs such as driving, equipment repair, inventory control, bookkeeping, etc.

In addition, we have our Career Ladder Program, where we train people for management positions within the company. There are three steps, culminating in Contract Manager — which is well compensated and involves tremendous responsibility.

Q: *Couldn't Tasks do a better job of helping people prepare to leave?*

A: That's a design question. Should a peewee basketball program be designed around the needs of the one kid in a million who will play in the NBA? Or for the rest of the kids who want to have fun and grow up to get regular jobs? If I (or Dr. Fairweather, for that matter) were going to design a program to move people on to something else, I would start by cataloguing the skills they will need. If I wanted them to live by themselves in an apartment, in a high-crime neighborhood, taking their meds sporadically, I would train them in watching television, avoiding contact with strangers, and accessing emergency services. Instead, we provide the best jobs and best homes in the nicest neighborhoods we can find, and we encourage people to make friends.

Q: *Wouldn't people be better off living independently?*

A: No. The so-called "independent" lifestyle promoted by our mental health system is not a step up at all; it is a step down from the rich, productive, interdependent lifestyle of a lodge. It is a positive thing when people leave because their mental illness was cured, when they leave the lodge because they found a nicer, cheaper place to live, or when they leave Tasks Unlimited for a better job. But these are extremely rare events. When people leave I wish them the best of luck, but there are certain risks.

Q: *You mean they might not succeed?*

A: If they merely return to the lodge in the same shape as they left, it was worth a try. But it often turns out worse. Without the support of the lodge, many people stop taking their meds correctly. They also don't eat or sleep as well. At a minimum, this leads to an exacerbation of their symptoms, and often a full-blown psychotic episode. And each psychotic episode involves a significant risk, maybe 10-20%, of incomplete recovery (the research isn't good in this area). People don't respond to medications as well the second time around; and some of the cognitive disorganization associated with psychosis may be residual. Plus, there is a risk of even worse things happening.

Q: *So you are saying a person with serious mental illness should stay in a lodge forever because of these risks?*

A: As I said earlier, it's not my call. Choice is the first and inviolable principle of a free society. Lodge members can choose to leave at any time, they can leave the lodge and keep their job with Tasks Unlimited, they can stay in the lodge and get a different job.

> OUR GOAL AT TASKS UNLIMITED IS TO ENHANCE CLIENT CHOICE, NEVER LIMIT IT.

Lodge members have all the choices available to anyone else with serious mental illness — plus a few extras. They can choose not to be poor, for example.

Q: *How can you call these success stories if the schizophrenia, etc., doesn't go away?*

A: Diabetes, lymphoma, advancing age — none of these things go away. Which doesn't mean that an aging person with diabetes and/or lymphoma can't be a success. With the right supports in place, people with schizophrenia can enjoy life and work and friends. I call that success.

APPENDIX II
*My vision for the future
of Tasks Unlimited*

The few people who leave the lodge are generally seeking to
evade the stigma of being in a mental health program. They
often end up with lower quality housing with less support and a
worse job or no job at all. They don't choose this because they
are stupid; they are just more troubled by the stigma which
taints any mental health program. I wish people didn't think
of us as a "mental health program."

Currently, most people think of Tasks as a residential
mental health program with a vocational component. Our
greatest admirers think of us as a terrific consumer-directed
residential program which sponsors three consumer-managed
affirmative businesses and produces spectacular hospital-
recidivism and client-employment outcomes. No matter
how good we are, however, we can only become a better and
better "mental health program."

My vision is to change the paradigm entirely. I would
like, someday, for people to think of Tasks Unlimited as a good,
solid business services company, with one heck of an employee
assistance program; and to think of lodges as a housing option
(along the lines of a condominium or a cooperative) with one
heck of a tenant support network.

This is not my original vision. I borrowed it from a
long-time lodge member — the inspiration for Warren of the
Diamond Lodge. In "That's Residential," Warren makes the
point that he doesn't really mind living in a group, it's the group

home he objects to. Warren also doesn't mind being a janitor; dentists get paid more, but janitorial work is less stressful. What really bothers him, what really hurts, what he can't imagine ever getting comfortable with — is being in a program.

What we need is a package of supportive services, "mental health" services if you will, that don't look or feel like mental health services. We need a package of services which attach unobtrusively to our housing and our employment without looking or feeling like a program. It's the program, the mere feel of a program, that drives people out of the lodge. I have not figured out where the money to replace our mental health funding will come from. I'm not even certain that weaning the lodges off of mental health funding would be enough to eliminate the stigma.

All I know is that the lodge is a terrific model. While it doesn't cure anyone's schizophrenia or bi-polar disorder, it allows people to lead healthy, productive lives in spite of such diseases. In the language of the Americans with Disabilities Act, the lodge is "a reasonable accommodation to the disability." The lodge, in its optimal form, provides high quality housing and solid, earn-a-living jobs. It provides friends, relationships, responsibility, stability, and a reason to feel optimistic about the future. Fiscally, the lodge is a bargain for both the public and the participant.

The last frontier is to free the lodge from the stigma of being a mental health program.

Richard Saholt is an Outsider Artist — his work is on display at the American Visionary Art Museum. He was awarded a Bronze star for his heroism in World War II; and 30-years later received a service-connected disability for schizophrenia.

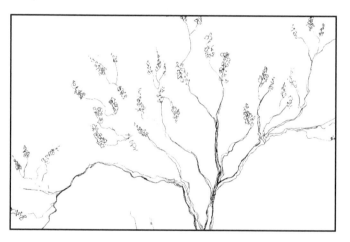

Rhoda Ostermann is an artist and energy-based healer living in Minneapolis. She has struggled with mental illness and found much healing for herself and others through her art.

For more information about Tasks Unlimited or Fairweather Lodges, consider visiting their **web sites** at:

WWW.TASKSUNLIMITED.ORG and **WWW.CCL.ORG**

or **writing** to:

Tasks Unlimited
2419 Nicollet Ave. So.
Minneapolis, MN 55407

or

Coalition for Community Living
2658 Roseland Avenue
East Lansing, MI 48823